Starlight, Time and the New Physics

How we can see starlight in our young universe

John Hartnett Ph.D.

CREATION
BOOK PUBLISHERS

Published and distributed by
Creation Book Publishers

www.creationbookpublishers.com

ISBN: 978-0-949906-68-7

Most scripture quotations from the New International Version
(NIV), Copyright © 1973, 1978, 1984 by International Bible
Society.

Cover design by Jay Paul, illustrations by John Hartnett or
Jay Paul unless otherwise noted.

Layout by Amanda Greenslade, with thanks to Rik Hilverts, Jes
Cardy and Jay Paul.

Printed: September 2007

For information on this book or on creation/evolution issues,
contact:

(addresses last page)

www.CreationOnTheWeb.com

Once in a generation ...

'Once in a generation comes something so new and so important that the contributors are remembered for generations to come. Carmeli and Hartnett, I predict, will be two of those names that take their place amongst the great names in physics. Carmeli, because he extended Einstein's theory of relativity to include the expansion of space, and Hartnett, because he took Carmeli's work and demonstrated the astounding conclusions that arise from it when the universe is viewed from the biblical perspective. The idea that God created the universe in six days just a few thousand years ago is now not only intellectually respectable, it's a far better explanation for what we observe than its competitors.'

—Alex Williams

Former consultant (and Australian representative) to the United Nations' International Atomic Energy Agency, and co-author of *Dismantling the Big Bang: God's Universe Rediscovered.*

Stunning revelations ...

'Having long followed the various creationist attempts to explain how we can see distant starlight in a universe that is a few thousand years old, I believe we are witnessing a bright new dawn in "creation physics". Some of the revelations in this book are simply stunning—and all the more exciting because the author has had a number of his papers on the new physics published in reputable secular journals. This book is a tremendous example of "thinking God's thoughts after Him" (usually attributed to the great creationist astronomer Johannes Kepler) and I heartily commend it.'

—Philip Bell

Scientist, speaker and CEO of *Creation Ministries International (UK/Europe).*

Acknowledgments

I am extremely grateful to Dr Carl Wieland for his inspiration and encouragement to complete this book and for his comments, his suggestions and for editing the text. Thanks also to Dr Jonathan Sarfati for his valuable comments and suggestions, to Kym Holwerda for stylistic and proof corrections and to Amanda Greenslade for her perseverence to complete the layout in record time.

  —Dr John Hartnett

   Physicist/cosmologist and speaker for
   Creation Ministries International (Australia).

Contents

About the Author 6

Chapter 1: Introduction 9

Chapter 2: Starlight and time 17

Chapter 3: 'Dark' matter—today's 'fudge
factor' 33

Chapter 4: Einstein and beyond 55

Chapter 5: Our galaxy—at the centre of the
action 73

Chapter 6: Stretched out the heavens 91

Chapter 7: Why we see starlight in a 'young'
universe 107

Technical Appendices

App. 1: The large scale structure of the
universe does not need 'dark' matter
or 'dark' energy 122

App. 2: The large scale structure of the
universe tested against high redshift
supernova measurements 135

App. 3: Spiral galaxy rotation curves explained
without 'dark' matter 157

App. 4: A finite bounded universe with a
unique centre 181

App. 5: The Galaxy at the centre of concentric
spherical shells of galaxies 199

App. 6: Light-travel-time problem
solved 219

About the author

John G. Hartnett received both his B.Sc. (hons) and his Ph.D. with distinction from the Department of Physics at the University of Western Australia (UWA) in the city of Perth. He works with the Frequency Standards and Metrology research group at the same university, where he holds the rank of Associate Professor (the equivalent of Reader in the UK, which would be Full Professor in the USA).

Dr Hartnett's research interests include the development of ultra-stable cryogenically cooled microwave oscillators based on a sapphire crystal, ultra-low-noise radar, tests of fundamental theories of physics such as Special and General Relativity and measurement of drift in fundamental constants and their cosmological implications.

John has a keen interest in cosmology and how it applies to the biblical creationist worldview. In addition, his work in the ongoing development of new physics has attracted the interest, and funding, of the university. This work establishes that there is no need to assume the existence of 'dark' matter or 'dark' energy to explain observations in the universe, and is the basis of the material in this book.

Dr Hartnett has published more than 120 papers in scientific journals and holds two patents. He is also a part-time speaker for *Creation Ministries International*, and is an effective communicator on the relevance of creation to the gospel and the implications of evolutionary teaching in society today.

The author (right) at the James Clerk Maxwell Telescope (below right) on the summit of Hawaii's extinct volcano, Mauna Kea. This 15 m telescope, located at 4,200 m (14,000 ft) above the clouds, operates in the submillimetre range of frequencies. The visit was in relation to joint research on cosmology and, subject to the success of a grant application, to the implementation of a cryogenic sapphire oscillator for VLBI on the mountain.

Chapter 1:

Introduction

Chapter 1: Introduction

Biblical creationists (Christians who believe the Bible and its history) have long been concerned about *the time of travel of light across the vast distances of the visible universe* within the six thousand years since the creation.

We live in a universe that is truly enormous in size. So large that distances are commonly measured in *light-years*. One light-year is the distance light travels in one year. Light travels very fast indeed; so fast, in fact, that we don't normally perceive it in our daily experience. Yet it has been measured at about 300,000 kilometres (about 186,000 miles) per second. This means that a light-year represents a distance of about ten trillion kilometres (six trillion miles).

I don't dispute the commonly held view that the visible universe is about twenty-eight billion light-years across (i.e. its diameter). At first glance, that would mean it should take a beam of light about fourteen billion years to travel to us from the outer limits of the universe (i.e. along its radius).

The Bible tells us (in Genesis 1) that the earth was created four days before the creation of the stars in the universe. It also reveals the time when our oldest ancestor Adam lived—God created him only two days after the stars, on the fourth day of Creation Week. So, considering the size of the universe, questions arise: 'How did Adam see the stars?' or 'How do *we* see distant stars?' For creationists this has been one of the most difficult problems to solve if we are to accept Genesis at face value, i.e. the way the Lord Jesus and all the New Testament writers took it, as well as most of the Church Fathers and all the Reformers—as straightforward history.[1] Even the nearest star (other than our sun) is 4.3 light-years away, and most of the rest of the stars in our galaxy are hundreds to thousands, even tens of thousands, of light-years away. And *from the biblical text alone*, we cannot determine a period of time greater than about seven thousand years since the creation of the universe. Most biblical scholars conclude that the text is intended to convey to us that little more than six thousand years have passed since the creation of all things.[2]

But this would seem to mean that we would only be able to see out into space to a distance of about six thousand light-years, or about a quarter of the distance to our galaxy's centre—certainly we shouldn't be able to see the cosmos with all its wonders *as we do*. Modern telescopes like the Hubble Space Telescope (HST) in orbit above Earth's atmosphere, and the group of four 8-metre telescopes at high altitude in the Atacama desert in Chile, called the Very Large Telescope (VLT), have revolutionized our view of the heavens. Truly 'the heavens declare the glory of God' as the psalmist tells us. But how do we see the stars and galaxies in the universe, *most* of which are much more distant than the six- or seven-thousand-light-year limit?

For some, this has been reason to disbelieve the straightforward meaning of Genesis and compromise with the origins teachings of so-called modern science, which does not hold to the view that the universe started with God creating *ex nihilo*, as described in Genesis. For them, it has been this 'intractable' problem that has caused them to abandon the Bible as the arbiter of real history. Yet it was only the belief in a consistent and lawful creation, a concept straight from the history given in the Bible, that made scientists strive to understand this creation in the first instance. It is no coincidence that modern science blossomed in Western Europe following the Reformation's emphasis on the Bible, as many secular philosophers agree,[3] because Christianity provides the presuppositions necessary for science to work.[4]

Science is a wonderful tool, but scientific explanations, even ones that seem as straightforward as the notion that light must take ten billion years to travel ten billion light-years, are always tentative. The history of science is littered with instances in which a previously assured 'fact' was overturned in a subsequent generation. And the universe, including the created laws that describe the way it normally operates, often turns out to be far more ingeniously constructed, and at the same time elegant, than previously imagined.

Given that, and given the way in which the history in the Bible is authenticated by the Lord Jesus Christ, the Creator Himself, we should therefore think carefully before assuming that a seeming 'fact' should overturn the authority of the Word of God. In a world in which we have been stunned by the notions of relativity, and mystified by the counter-intuitive results of quantum mechanics, is it not more likely that there is an explanation we have not thought of yet? One of my non-physicist friends in creation ministry often tells his hearers: 'I would not like to have to stand in front of the Creator at the end of time and have to admit, "Lord, I didn't trust what your Word so clearly said, merely because my feeble mind couldn't work out how you (God) could possibly have done the trick of making a universe that was both very large and very young."' In short, when there is an apparent conflict between science and a clear teaching of the Bible, we need to humbly assume that it is more likely that our understanding of the universe is deficient. When we do this, i.e. use biblical history as our starting point, we will be led to a greater understanding of His universe, as this book shows.

'Everyone knows ... '

There was a time when 'everybody knew' that the sun travelled around the earth—it was a 'fact of observation'. When some people pointed out that the motions of the planets did not seem to fit that picture, instead of looking for another explanation (after all, that might mean abandoning the 'fact of observation'), people just invented even *more* complicated theories ('epicycles') to 'explain away' these inconvenient observations.

In this book, we show that a similar thing happened in more recent times in regard to astronomy—complicated explanations were invented to 'explain away' inconvenient facts. When Newton's seemingly all-conquering laws of physics failed to explain certain astronomical observations, scientists dreamed up various 'fudge factors', such as an unknown hidden planet, to explain the discrepancy. In reality, what was needed was new physics that would still encompass Newton's laws, but expand our understanding—this arrived with Einstein.

In our day, a similar thing is happening, in another area—one which is not only instructive as background, but one which provides a major key to resolving the starlight travel issue. As this book will show, because of the insistence by the majority on the unbiblical 'big bang' model, a whole new suite of 'fudge factors' has been postulated to explain certain puzzling observations. These fudge factors include unknown and invisible ('dark') forms of matter and even energy. Once again, the point is that what is needed is new physics. Similarly, if we take the starlight travel issue, not as some impossible conundrum, but rather as an *observation* to be explained (we *do* see distant starlight in a cosmos which *is* only thousands of years old), then it is clear that here, too, new physics is required. In this book, I will introduce you, in an understandable way, to new physics that does away with the need for the big bangers' mysterious 'dark' fudge factors—and almost as a neat 'aside', it resolves the starlight/time issue.

This new physics, which does away with all those 'fudge factors', fits what we observe on all scales in the universe and is consistent with Einstein's relativity theory. And what 'falls out' of the very same equations is an explanation of how light can traverse the vast reaches of the cosmos in only a matter of days (see chapter 7). It indicates that Adam would most definitely have been able to see the stars in our galaxy (the Milky Way) *very* shortly after he was created.

References

1. For a brief but powerful summary, see the popular booklet *15 Reasons to Take Genesis as History*, by Don Batten and Jonathan Sarfati (*Creation Ministries International*).
2. This includes many so-called liberal scholars who, though they do not believe the text of Genesis to be true, readily point out what it was *clearly meant to convey*: six ordinary-length earth-rotation days, a global flood and a universe thousands of years old.
3. Stark, R., *For The Glory of God: How Monotheism Led to Reformations, Science, Witch-hunts and the End of Slavery,* Princeton University Press, USA, 2003; Stark R., *The Victory of Reason: How Christianity Led to Freedom, Capitalism, and Western Success,* Random House, NY, USA, 2006.
4. Batten and Sarfati, ref.1, pp. 25ff.

Chapter 2:

Starlight and time

Chapter 2: Starlight and time

The starlight-travel-time problem was significantly addressed by Russ Humphreys in his popular book *Starlight and Time*.[1] Certainly the 1994 publication of his book will go down in history as a turning point. His cosmological model attempted to give an explanation for the creationist problem in a 'young' universe. Humphreys helped us search 'outside of the box.' The 'box', in this case, was the idea that time is absolute. We needed to be reminded that relativity has long taught us that time and space are not universal absolutes but depend on the circumstances of the observer. In this case, the rate at which time flows is not the same everywhere in the universe.

Humphreys described a situation where the universe could be considered to be a gravitational well with all the galaxies distributed around the well and our galaxy in the bottom at the centre (see fig. 2.1). The universe is finite, with an edge—a boundary beyond which there are no galaxies—but there is space beyond. He had the universe expanding from a white hole (a black hole running in reverse, with matter pouring out instead of falling in), permitted by the equations of relativity. In such a universe, due to well-known and tested effects of gravity, the light we see coming from the outer limits of the universe should be blueshifted. This means that the photons gain energy as they fall down the gravitational well. This then provided a mechanism for time-dilation. That means that clocks in the cosmos would run faster than the same type of clocks on Earth. No detail was

Figure 2.1: Gravitational potential well from a spherically symmetric distribution of galaxies with our galaxy at the centre. (Schematic only and not to scale.)

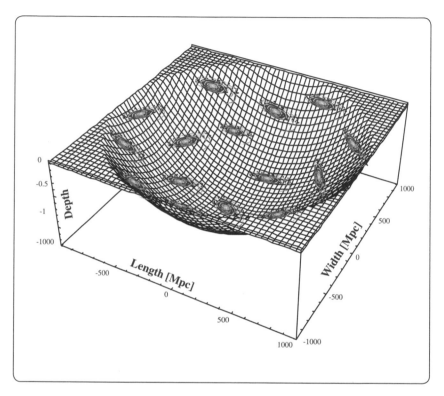

provided in the book, and it appears now that this mechanism does not give sufficient time-dilation. Nevertheless, I see *Starlight and Time* as a first step towards the correct understanding of the cosmos, and towards a potential solution to the light-travel-time problem. But as Humphreys himself readily and repeatedly acknowledged, it was only the beginning.

It was, he said, meant to stimulate others to look into this new direction of creation cosmology—and it certainly achieved that. In such a 'time dilation' model, the key is that the universe is only thousands of years old—but relativity leads us to ask, '*By which clocks?*'[2] The answer is clear, namely that the focus of Genesis history is on *earth clocks*. From the perspective of an observer on the earth, therefore, it is possible that the entire universe can be only six thousand years old, while there is 'plenty of time' for light, travelling at today's constant speed in local frames of reference,[3] to cover a distance of billions of light-years. It is only necessary to show how such time-dilation would have occurred, i.e. what the mechanism was that would have made earth clocks run at such different speeds to cosmic clocks.

In 1998, Humphreys significantly modified his model with the publication of *New Vistas*.[4] There he found in his equations a 'timeless region' where clocks stopped for different phases of the expansion of the universe. This mechanism provided the needed time for the photons to travel most of the distance in the cosmos. It worked primarily where the universe was very compact, and unusual effects on the time dimension occurred. That is, in some regions time behaved like a spatial dimension; hence clocks remained suspended while the expansion continued.

However, the model, though still not fully developed and lacking detail, could not offer a clear explanation for the travel-time of light in the region of space very close to our galaxy, within a few million light-years of Earth.[5] This can be understood in terms of the galaxies that are close to ours, at the centre of the gravitational well, as shown in fig. 2.1. The light we see from our neighbour, the Andromeda galaxy, for example, which is about two and a half million light-years away, should provide the information we need about both the expansion of the universe there as well as any time dilation. But, due to the small local motion of this galaxy towards our own galaxy, its light is slightly blueshifted. If there was a vast amount of time-dilation due to our galaxy being much deeper in the potential well, then we should see it in the starlight—we should see a much greater blueshift. To explain the light-travel time, it seems his model still needs more work.

Before Humphreys, a common solution was the suggestion that the speed of light was enormously faster around Creation Week and has slowed down since (c-decay[6]). Let's be clear. The speed of an object is simply equal to the distance it travels in the time allotted.

$$\text{Speed} = \text{Distance} \div \text{Time} \qquad (2.1)$$

If the speed of light is constant and the distance is known, then the time it travels can easily be determined. This is what has led many to conclude that the vast ages are real. They would reason that since many stars are millions/billions of light-years away (as I agree), and since light travels at a constant speed, the time conclusion is beyond question.[7]

However, some have suggested that the speed of light was much greater in the past. R.E. Kofahl[8] describes an appealing scenario of the heavens being stretched out, and the speed of light being up to 600 billion times the present value. But this presents a problem: if the speed of light slowed down, how is it that we are now able to see the stars? They would have disappeared from view. The stars provide us with information in the same starlight that we receive in our telescopes. If the speed of light was enormously faster in the past, we should be able to detect that in the starlight. Unless a plausible mechanism can be demonstrated that doesn't lead to absurd physical implications, these types of scenarios will always fail.

The underlying problem may be a reluctance by creationist cosmologists to break with the idea that time is absolute and that it has always flowed at a constant rate throughout the universe. Humphreys' white-hole model made such a break and has generally been well received by creationists. Probably this is because his model involves accelerated time increments happening in the cosmos *during* 24-hour periods on Earth. It needs to be made very clear that it may have been that in the cosmos billions of years of ordinary Earth time passed, while only six 24-hour days passed on Earth. More detail is still needed and a fit with observational data has yet to be demonstrated for Humphreys' model. But the model uses an 'economy of miracles' and instead heavily relies on a particular solution of Einstein's field equations from general relativity to explain the mechanics of the cosmos.

As an argument against the validity of long ages in the universe and for recent creation, it is not uncommon for creationist authors to point out some astrophysical feature that is inconsistent with the assumed long ages in big bang cosmology. For example, the high dispersion velocities of stars in galaxies;[9] or that spiral galaxies, which are slowly winding themselves up, should have been 'fully wound' if the cosmos were billions of years old. The authors then use this as evidence for short ages (i.e. six thousand years) in the cosmos, consistent with a creationist view. But especially with the advent of time-dilation models, care is needed to ensure that a particular argument is valid within the framework of the particular creationist model one adopts. For example, say one has a Humphreys-type model with time running faster in the cosmos than on Earth—and, as a result, billions of years can pass in the cosmos while thousands pass on Earth. In such a model, one can't just blithely say, 'There's enough time in the cosmos for the light to get to us, but there isn't enough for the galaxies to still be unwound.' That would be like having one's cake and eating it, too.[10] It may be, of course, that within the framework of a particular time-dilation model, there is still insufficient 'cosmic time' for the observed spirals to remain unwound. In the alleged big bang history, all galaxies in the universe formed at the same epoch only a billion years after the big bang, which is alleged to have occurred about 13.7 billion years ago. So the question may still be asked: 'Why are there still spirals—why haven't they all wound up?'[11] This would still be a valid creationist argument. But care to ensure self-consistency is essential or we have no argument.

As a matter of fact, big bangers can scarcely point the finger at creationists over this problem, because they have a light-travel-time problem, too. Known as the 'horizon problem', it arises because points in the universe that are now separated by billions of light-years are all at the same temperature.[12] For temperature to equalize between two points, radiation must travel between them, and some of these points are so far apart that, even given the big bang's assumed multi-billion-year age, there has been nowhere near enough time for the radiation to cover the distance, even at the speed of light. Some of the solutions proposed, such as a massively higher speed of light in the past, or rapid inflation,[13] have been no less exotic than any put forward by creationists.

The options

I believe that there are five possible areas of explanation for the solution to the starlight-travel-time problem, all consistent with the text of Genesis, that still maintain the 6 × 24-hour literal days of creation. These are summarized below in no particular order.

1. Phenomenological language

The first possibility is that the language of Genesis is phenomenological language (describing appearance). In this case, stars were made billions of years before Day 4, but in such a manner that the light from all stars, no matter how far away, all arrived at the earth on Day 4 and so could have been seen first at that moment. This is then a reference frame 'time-stamping' events from the moment they are seen on Earth. Lisle's time convention[14] describes this idea. The long-term survival of his model, in my opinion, lies with scriptural interpretation; for example, whether the phenomenological view is consistent with Exodus 20:9, 11, which reads:

> 'Six days you shall labour, and do all your work: For in six days the Lord made heaven and earth, the sea, and all that in them is, and rested the seventh day ... .'

The word 'all' seems to restrict the work being done in creating things to the Creation Week period, where six 24-hour days pass on Earth. The phenomenological interpretation puts the actual physical creation of the stars before the six days begin and is 'seen' as happening on the fourth day on Earth. I would also note that Lisle's physical interpretation is questionable and I have elaborated on this in published correspondence.[15]

2. Faster clocks 'out there'

The second possibility is that clocks in the cosmos in the past have run at much higher rates than clocks on Earth. Especially during Creation Week, clocks of the exact same type on the edge of the universe ran something like a trillion times faster than clocks on Earth, and therefore light from such regions had plenty of time to get to Earth in a matter of days, not millions or billions of years.

Burgess[16] describes a rapid aging process for stars and a faster speed of light. It was all accelerated, like fast-forwarding a video tape. And, after all the light information reached the earth, the rates were reduced to what we now measure. The problem with this model, as we have already hinted at earlier, is that the stars would disappear from view as the light slowed down, and then subsequently take millions and billions of years to get here. Also, such light arriving at the earth would show enormous observable blueshifts.[17] But it doesn't. A more ingenious mechanism is needed to overcome such obvious objections.

This hypothesis is not as simple as it first seems, and the light coming from the cosmos carries information that makes the model testable. We can compare clock rates on Earth today with clock rates in source galaxies and we should still see a difference. Light from those sources that have faster clock rates should be blueshifted compared to Earth clocks. It is not. Were it true, we would need to find a physical explanation that could support the idea and allow us to see redshifts in an expanding universe.

3. Clocks slower here than 'out there'

The third possibility is that clocks on Earth in the past ran at much slower rates than clocks in the cosmos. Especially if, during the Creation Week, clocks of the exact same type on Earth ran about a trillion times slower than clocks at the edge of the universe; then light from the edge of the universe would have had plenty of time to get to Earth in a matter of days, as recorded by Earth clocks, not millions or billions of years. Humphreys' model is of this type. The perception of time to someone on the earth looking at astronomical clocks during this period would be that they are running very quickly.

The hypothesis is simpler than the previous one and *not equivalent*. Consider the clock rates at emission and reception. In the former (category 2), clocks in the distant cosmos were running faster than Earth clocks now run at reception. In this case (category 3), at emission, clocks in the distant cosmos were running at the same rate as Earth clocks now run at reception. Only during a day (or two) of Creation Week were Earth clocks running slower on receiving the light. The light we are seeing now is that which originated during the creation process but from sources in the cosmos where the clock rates were essentially the same as they are now on Earth.

It is important to realize that this description requires that the universe have a preferred frame of reference. And there is evidence that this is the case. It appears the Earth is actually near the centre of the universe.[18] This is developed in Chapter 5. The language of Genesis puts the Earth in a 'reference frame' that is special, in the centre of God's will and plan, so it is quite consistent to find that it is physically in a special location, too. The model suggested in this book is of this type.

4. *c*-decay

The fourth possibility is that the speed of light ('c') was enormously faster in the past, of the order of a trillion times its current value. This may have been the case during Creation Week and then the light slowed enormously to the present value. Again this model is testable, especially with astronomical observations, such as measurements of the fine structure constant. This hypothesis has been advanced in the past by creationists, Setterfield and Norman,[6] who placed considerable weight on the precision of a few historical astronomical determinations of the speed of light. The idea that c was originally faster is currently in vogue in the secular community,[19] but they are not dealing with timescales on Earth of only six thousand years. Also, the secular advocates of past higher c rely on an apparent change in a constant which the Setterfield/ Norman theory predicts should *not* change.[20] In short, the observational evidence available to us today clearly precludes this model.[21, 22] It is absolutely not viable, unless there is, and has been, a complicated balance of changes in many 'so-called' constants over observable history. But Occam's razor[23] would tell us that this is not the case.

Another model in this category is the Harris model.[24] It starts with an infinite speed of light at creation. Then, after the Fall, it changes to the current value as a function of time and linear distance from Earth. Like an expanding bubble spreading out through the universe, the speed of light drops from an infinite value to the current value at the surface of the bubble. One problem with this model may be massive blueshifts resulting from a change of infinite to finite speed of light. Also, the fine structure of the atomic spectra must change from a stage of no fine structure to the current state as the bubble passes. This would be observable in starlight. It isn't. Humphreys and I both toyed with a finite speed version of this model but ran into other difficulties.

5. Light created 'on its way'

The fifth option results from the understanding that the Creator God revealed in the Bible *is* a God of miracles. It is probably true that if we were looking a miracle in the face we might try to reason a naturalistic mechanism for it. God does intervene in the physical world, and during those times the laws of physics are obviously 'put on hold'. However, I don't believe God engages in deception, and as we will see, the idea that He created all the light beams 'in place' involves that. This is because a beam of light also carries *information*. When a supernova[25] happens, for instance, we see a whole series of events take place—the information is transmitted by the light beams. If God created the beams of light along with their information, then if the supernova occurred more than 6,000 light-years away, that would mean that all that information we see, giving evidence of things happening, would have to be fraudulent—it never happened. It would mean that God had created a gigantic phony lightshow of things that are not real.

There is a way around this issue, a really complex and *ad hoc* miracle that would enable the creation of a beam of light from source to observer so that the observer appears to see current information. For example, when the supernova named 1987a occurred in the Large Magellanic Cloud, which is about 170,000 light-years distant, God could have miraculously translated the light across 170,000 light-years distance of space instantly (as if the photons had passed through a wormhole) and then just outside the solar system let it move at the usual speed of light. This hypothesis is untestable and, though not impossible, seems implausible, to put it mildly. Miracles in the Bible are rare and special events, the purpose of which is clearly understood and/or revealed. This does not fit that category; it looks more like a convenient set of miracles invented *ad hoc* to overcome a difficulty.

This book explores new physics that not only solves many current puzzles of the universe without any mysterious 'fudge factors' and with an excellent fit to observational data, but leads to the conclusion that time has been accelerated in the cosmos with respect to Earth's clocks. This could have been done through a supernatural acceleration of time, or, as we shall see is more likely to be the case, from God using his cosmos in such a way as Humphreys conjectured; a way that caused time to accelerate in the cosmos.

References

1. Humphreys, D.R., *Starlight and time*, Master Books, Colorado Springs, CO, 1994.
2. There is no absolute time. One cannot say, 'God's time', because God is outside of time—He created time.
3. This is the speed that any local observer would measure.
4. Humphreys, D.R., New vistas of space and time, *J. of Creation* **12**(2):195–212, 1998.
5. Hartnett, J.G., Look-back time in our galactic neighbourhood leads to a new cosmogony, *J. of Creation* **17**(1):73–79, 2003.
6. Norman, T. and Setterfield, B., The atomic constants, light and time, *SRI International Invited Research Report*, Menlo Park, CA, 1986.
7. Of course, even though 'distance' and 'speed' might be fixed, they haven't considered the possibility of time dilation, which affects the third variable.
8. Kofahl, R.E., Speculation concerning God's 'big bang', Letter to the Editor of *CRSQ* **39**:64, 2002.
9. Bernitt, R., Fast stars challenge big bang origin for dwarf galaxies, *J. of Creation* **14**(3):5–7, 2000.
10. Humphreys addresses this issue in: How do spiral galaxies and supernova remnants fit in with Dr Humphreys' cosmological model? <www.creationontheweb.com/windup>, 12 March 2007.
11. Astronomers no longer believe ellipticals wound up from earlier spiral forms because most have little angular motion. They are more like motionless blobs. However, in the time available to a spiral galaxy since the big bang, it could have wound around about 500 times.
12. The big bang model says that due to the random nature of the initial fireball these same points were not initially at the same temperature.
13. The idea is that the universe's expansion goes through a hyper-fast period, due to the onset of a phase transition in the fabric of space—the vacuum. The speed of light refers to motion of photons through the vacuum itself, so superluminal (faster-than-light) propagation is suggested to allow for the exchange of photons.
14. Newton, R. (authored under this pen-name by Jason Lisle), Distant starlight and Genesis: conventions of time measurement, *J. of Creation* **15**(1):80–85, 2001.
15. Hartnett, J.G., Distant starlight and Genesis: is 'observed time' a physical reality? *J. of Creation*, Letters **16**(3):65–68, 2002.

16. Burgess, S., *He made the stars also*, Day One Publications, Surrey, England, 2001.

17. If the light speed was much greater in the past, either the frequencies are now higher due to higher excitation energies of the sources or the received wavelengths are shortened by the Doppler effect. In either case, referenced against standard sources on Earth, such light, would appear blueshifted.

18. Not to be confused with geocentrism, the idea that the earth is stationary and provides an absolute reference frame, and all other bodies move around it.

19. Cho, A., Light may have slowed down, *Newscientist.com*, <www.newscientist.com/news/print.jsp?id=ns99991158>, 2001.

20. See <www.creationontheweb.com/cdk> in regard to the fine structure constant.

21. Hartnett, J.G., Is there any evidence for a change in *c*? Implications for creationist cosmology, *J. of Creation* **16**(3): 89–94, 2002.

22. Also, the rate of energy loss due to gravitational radiation would be proportional to *c*, yet the observed loss from a distant binary pulsar is consistent with *c* at current rates, not with the much faster *c* proposed by Setterfield at the time that radiation was emitted from the pulsars. Wanser, K., *Radioactive Decay Update: Breaking Down the Old-Age Paradigm* (DVD recorded at the Creation 2003 conference in West Harrison, Indiana).

23. Occam, William of Occam, or Ockham (1284–1347), was an English philosopher and theologian. His work on knowledge, logic and scientific inquiry played a major role in the transition from medieval to modern thought. He based scientific knowledge on experience and self-evident truths, and on logical propositions resulting from those two sources. In his writings, Occam stressed the Aristotelian principle that entities must not be multiplied beyond what is necessary. This principle became known as Occam's (or Ockham's) Razor or the law of parsimony. A problem should be stated in its most basic and simplest terms. In science, the simplest theory that fits the facts of a problem is the one that should be selected, <www.2think.org/occams_razor.shtml>.

24. Harris, D.M., A solution to seeing stars, *CRSQ* **15** (Sept):112–115, 1978.

25. An exploding star.

Chapter 3:

'Dark' matter—today's 'fudge factor'

Chapter 3: 'Dark' matter—today's 'fudge factor'

Mercury's orbit: how General Relativity beat Vulcan

Towards the close of the nineteenth century, astronomers noticed that the orbit of the planet Mercury was being perturbed and proposed that there was some unknown agency at work. When the (then standard) Newtonian physics was applied to its dynamics over a long period of time, a discrepancy was found in the amount the perihelion[1] would advance. Even though near circular, the orbit is slightly elliptical, and over centuries the ellipse would not retrace itself, but slightly advance, forming a Rosetta (see fig. 3.1). A certain amount of this advance was expected from the pull of the other planets, but there remained an unexplained anomalous portion. It was measured to be a minuscule 43 seconds of arc per century, yet it was a real problem for physicists trying to understand the dynamics of the heavenly bodies in the solar system.

The solution was to propose the presence of 'dark' matter that was unseen, yet was gravitationally perturbing the orbits of the inner planets. It seems that, like Ptolemy's epicycles, introduced to maintain the Earth-centred cosmology of Aristarchus in the pre-Copernican era, 'dark' matter was invented to keep the status quo. The form of the 'dark' matter envisaged by theorists of the day varied; some preferred an inner asteroid belt within Mercury's orbit and some an additional planet—the planet Vulcan, which was said to orbit very close to the sun (hence the name—see fig. 3.2), but in such a manner that it was always conveniently hidden from view by Earth observers, on the other side of the sun. (They didn't seem to mind that an object near Mercury would have a shorter orbital period than Earth.)

In 1915, with the publication of Einstein's general theory of relativity,[2] this problem was solved. In fact, Einstein was able to calculate exactly the 43 arcseconds. This meant that 'dark' matter was unnecessary and all that had been lacking was new, or I should say, the correct physics. Newton's physics was found wanting when space and time were warped significantly in the vicinity of the sun. This was the case for the orbit of the planet Mercury. Einstein's

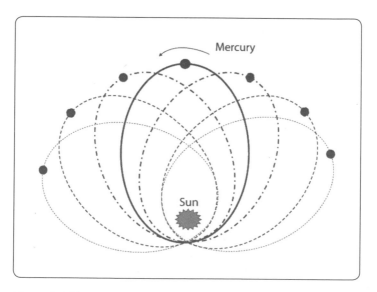

Figure 3.1: Mercury's orbit shown as a highly exaggerated ellipse. The orbit precesses slowly over time.

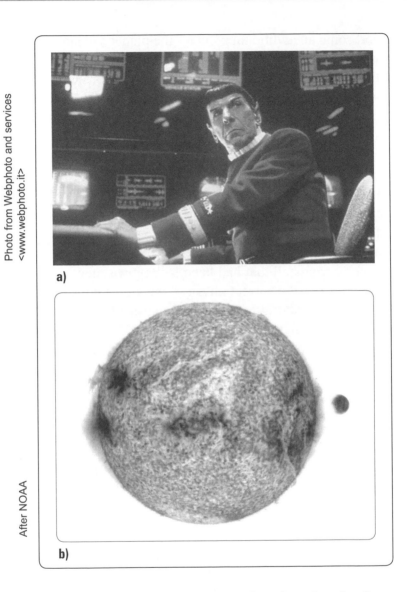

Photo from Webphoto and services
<www.webphoto.it>

a)

After NOAA

b)

Figure 3.2: a) Vulcan is Spock's home planet in modern-day *Star Trek*, b) Vulcan was believed to be a planet that orbited very close to the sun inside Mercury's orbit; hence a very hot planet.

physics was needed to solve the problem. I contend that we are seeing a similar problem again now on all scales in the universe.

Dynamical mass

Since Newton, astronomers have used

$$M = \frac{v^2 R}{G} \qquad (3.1)$$

to calculate the mass (M) of the sun and whatever planets are included inside the orbit of the test 'particle', which might be the earth, for example. In equation (3.1), v is the speed of the test 'particle' in orbit, R is the separation distance between the centres of the test 'particle' and the sun, and G is Newton's gravitational constant.

This Newtonian equation (3.1) can also be used to determine the masses of objects outside our solar system when they are considered to be in orbit around a central body (e.g. a star or nucleus of a galaxy). Masses can also be inferred from the amount of visible luminous material, but in fact the two methods disagree. The amount of mass calculated from the dynamics (motions) of stars within galaxies, for example, is always a lot more than what is observed. In other words, it always appears that there is 'missing' matter; stuff that we can't see.

Usually a mass-to-luminosity ratio (M/L) is calculated. This is the amount of matter from dynamical considerations compared with the luminous material of the source, but normalized to the mass-to-luminosity ratio of our sun. Therefore if an object were to have $M/L = 1$, no 'dark' matter would be needed and all the mass observed from the dynamics would be accounted for in the luminous material.

'Missing matter' on all scales

Table 3.1 shows the M/L ratios derived by different techniques and for different scale sizes in the universe.[3] It is clear that the ratio (M/L) here is far from unity. Therefore, it has been assumed that there is a lot of 'dark' matter inhabiting the regions of space within galaxies, in clusters and in super-clusters. In fact, the assumption is that most of the matter in the universe is the dark kind, which does not interact with radiation, but only has a gravitational effect.

We can see from table 3.1 how the problem actually gets far greater as we go up in scale. For many galaxies, the mass that we can 'see', i.e. the visible, luminous matter, is only one-tenth of that needed to explain the motions of the objects using standard physics.

The problem of 'missing' or 'dark' matter is there on the scale size of the universe as a whole, too. This has arisen from the need to fit the cosmological equations, describing the motion of the galaxies comprising the large-scale structure of the universe,

Table 3.1: *M/L* ratios derived from different techniques

Techniques	Radius (light-years)	*M/L*
Visible rotation curves of spiral galaxies	30 thousand	2–5
Radio rotation curves of spiral galaxies	30 thousand	5–10
Halos required to stabilize spiral models	30 thousand	4–12
Elliptical galaxies from internal velocity dispersion	3 thousand	5–12
Milky Way from satellite dwarf galaxies	600 thousand	40–70
Local galaxy group	2 million	40–80
Binary spiral galaxies	1.5 million	40–80
Small galaxy groups from velocity dispersions	1.5 million	40–90
Large clusters of galaxies	2–6 million	400–600

to the observed data, specifically the distances derived from a certain type of supernova, which employs presumed knowledge of the absolute intrinsic brightness of these stellar explosions.

Figure 3.3: Pie chart showing the alleged mass/energy content of the present universe based on Friedmann models

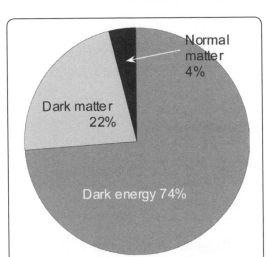

In astronomy, the standard method to determine distance is from the luminosity of standard sources, called 'standard candles'. As is well known, the inverse square law of illumination allows one to calculate the distance to a source if the absolute brightness (or magnitude) is known.

Astrophysicists, in recent years, have used what are called type Ia supernovae (SNe Ia) to establish the absolute brightness of the representative supernova[4] and hence test cosmological models in an expanding universe. In fact, an exact determination of the absolute brightness is not required, only the magnitude dependence on redshift, which is determined from the models under test.

Using modern versions of the Friedmann–Lemaître (FL) model, developed independently by Alexander

Friedmann and Georges Lemaître in the 1920s, it was determined at the end of 1998 that not only is the universe expanding, as Hubble first discovered, but also that it is accelerating.[5] However, to fit the FL theory to the data, 'dark' matter has been reinvented.[6]

When determined this way, this new 'dark' matter comprises about 22% of the mass/energy content of the universe. Put another way, 'dark' matter supposedly makes up 85% of the total matter content of the universe. There have been many proposals as to what it might be; some suggest exotic new particles (WIMPs[7]) and others massive normal-matter objects that we just can't see (MACHOs[8]).

'Dark' energy, too

As if this were not enough, it turns out that there is also another component needed, called 'dark' energy. This comprises about 74% of the mass/energy content of the universe! (See fig. 3.3.) Neither 'dark' matter nor 'dark' energy is known to modern physics, yet it is supposed to be all around us. Only the remaining 4% comprises the usual stuff we are made of; atoms, electrons, etc., called baryonic matter.

Cosmological Special Relativity

In the years predating Einstein's relativity theory, it was assumed that space and time were independent and that there existed a frame of reference, fixed in space, in which time had the universal property such that it would be the same for all observers, independent of their motion. Lorentz, Poincaré and Einstein broke that connection. In Einstein's special theory, the speed of light (in a vacuum) became a universal constant, *c*. Time and space became entwined as *spacetime,* which would warp according to the motion of the observer. No one observer's determination of when and where an event occurred was any longer absolute. Another observer moving with a different relative velocity would determine the sequence of events differently. This seemed crazy at the time but it has been borne out with many experiments over many decades since then. Later, Einstein took this a step further by adding the effects of gravity to these dimensions of the universe, which introduced the idea of curvature to *spacetime.* This development is what led to a theoretical understanding of the anomalous motion of the planet Mercury.

Carmeli's new theory

In the early 1990s, a theoretical physicist, Moshe Carmeli, extended this concept to the cosmos. Though he was in his early sixties, he developed a new description of the universe around the kitchen table in his home in Beer Sheba, Israel. Being from the old school, he did most of his calculations on paper. He had spent most of his early years working on Einstein's special and general theories and has published a number of detailed books on relativity.[9]

Carmeli observed that there are really only two things that astronomers actually measure: distance and velocity. In fact, generally, they are both derived in turn from other measurements, like the apparent magnitudes (brightness) and redshifts of sources. (See chapter 4 for an explanation of redshift.) On the largest scales of the universe, he saw that astronomers really could only take still pictures of the galaxies as they are seen in the sky. From these pictures, the redshifts are derived and then, using the Hubble Law, distances are determined. From this, he initially developed his new theory: cosmological special relativity (CSR),[10] and then his general theory, which included matter.

In 1996, using his new theory, which is explained in more detail in Chapter 4, Carmeli predicted[11] that the universe must be accelerating. This was almost two years before the observations determined it to be so. Carmeli's new *spacevelocity* is an extension to Einstein's general theory, which incorporates a new dimension, the velocity of the expanding fabric of space itself. His general theory incorporates all of Einstein's theory that has been found valid for our solar system at least, but extends it to the larger scales of the Galaxy and the cosmos.

Using his new metric,[12] Carmeli was able to replicate the form of the observed data from the high redshift type Ia supernova teams. In turn, I have been able to extend that treatment and, by properly describing the matter density dependence on redshift, eliminate the need for 'dark' matter on the scale of the cosmos as a whole.[13] Also, Carmelian cosmology does not explicitly incorporate a 'dark' energy term. 'Dark' energy really has resulted from the application of incorrect physics to the large-scale structure of the cosmos. Using the correct physics, what has been perceived as 'dark' energy is really a description of the properties of the vacuum itself. Vacuum

Figure 3.4: Carmeli's books *Cosmological Special Relativity* *Cosmological Relativity*

World Scientific Publishing Company

is not 'nothing' and it has properties that the new metric (i.e. new physics) correctly incorporates. (See Appendix 1.)

I have also applied this theory to the actual observational data[14] and have found that normal matter density equals only about 4% of the critical matter density of the universe. This is the same as the small amount of normal baryonic matter we observe in the luminous matter. No 'dark' matter at all is required. (See Chapter 4 and Appendix 2.) The fits to the observational data are far better than those used to fit to the standard Friedmann–Lemaître models. The new Carmeli–Hartnett model eliminates the need for any exotic 'dark' matter at all. In fact, the model requires that the universe be of low matter density as observed. For an in-depth study, I recommend the books *Cosmological Special Relativity*,[15] *Cosmological Relativity*[16] and the Appendices in this book.

Problem of 'dark' matter in galaxies

Rotation curves highlighted by the circular motion of stars—or more accurately characterized by the spectroscopic detection of the motion of neutral hydrogen and other gases in the disk regions of spiral galaxies—have caused concern for astronomers for many decades.

Newtonian physics predicts that the farther the orbiting object (e.g. star or gas molecule) from the central mass (e.g. nuclear bulge of galaxy), the lower the speed it travels. The orbital speeds should be much lower than those measured in the disk regions of spiral galaxies. We know this to be true in our solar system. Mercury and Venus travel around the sun much faster than the outer planets, like Uranus or Neptune. However, when the circular speeds of the stars and gases in the disk region of a spiral galaxy are measured as a function of the distance from its centre (see fig. 3.5), it is noted that in general the circular speeds of the test 'particles' increase as one measures speeds of these particles farther from the centre of the galaxy. The speeds rise to a maximum, sometimes start to fall as the radial distance increases, but mostly they continue at some constant value. The plots of speed versus distance from the centre are called *rotation curves*. They are anomalous because we expect the particle speeds to eventually trail off to zero at great distances from the centre of the galaxy.

Most luminous galaxies show slightly declining rotation curves in the regions outside the star-bearing disk, coming down from a broad maximum in the disk. Intermediate mass galaxies have mostly nearly flat rotation speeds along the disk radius. Lower luminosity galaxies usually have monotonically increasing orbital velocities across the disk.[17] The traditional solution has been to invoke halo 'dark' matter[18] that surrounds the galaxy but is transparent to all forms of electromagnetic radiation. (See fig. 3.5.) In fact, astronomers have traditionally resorted to 'dark' matter whenever known laws of physics are unable to explain the observed dynamics. The halo supposedly takes the form of a spherical distribution around the galaxy but requires a cusp-like density distribution. But in fact, little 'dark' matter is needed in the centre of the galaxy; mostly located in the

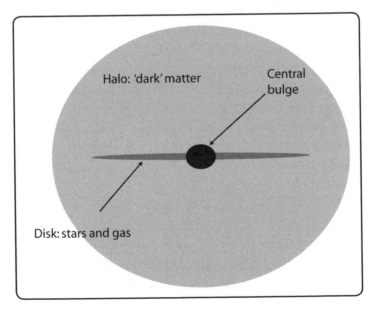

Figure 3.5: Schematic of halo 'dark' matter around spiral galaxy

halo away from the centre. Even big-bang-believing astrophysicists believe this to be very contrived, and some have sought a solution.

In 1983, Milgrom introduced his MOND,[19] an empirical approach which attempts to modify Newtonian dynamics in the region of very low acceleration. Newton's law describes a force proportional to the reciprocal of the radial separation *squared*, but Milgrom finds that a law proportional to the reciprocal of the radial separation *only* fits the data very well. However, Milgrom had no underlying theory.[20] Others have also attempted to formulate modified force laws, such as Disney,[21] Wright and Disney,[22] and Carmeli.

Carmeli formulated a 5-dimensional modification and extension of Einstein's general theory, where the Hubble expansion imposes an additional constraint on the motion of particles and hence the dynamics in galaxies. He was able to derive the well-known Tully–Fisher relation,[23] which says the fourth power of the rotation speed of a galaxy[24] is proportional to its luminosity. In fact, Carmeli showed the relationship was with the mass of the galaxy, which is assumed to be related to its luminosity. The Tully–Fisher relation is considered to be so reliable in astronomy that it is routinely used to measure the distance to a galaxy, because it gives a measure of the brightness of the source. This would be a strange coincidence if all galaxies had just the right amount of 'dark' matter to give rise to this relation, but not if there was an underlying theory to explain it.

As a result, the new theory questioned the existence of 'dark' matter, but Carmeli stopped short of the necessary equations to describe the motions of the gases and stars that are used as tracers for the calculation of the dynamical masses. I was again able to extend his theory, deriving a post-Newtonian equation that was able to produce the typical galaxy-rotation curves[25] (see Appendix 3). The theory *then accounted for the alleged missing mass without the need for 'dark' matter* (on the galactic scale). The amount accounted for was in the range of $M/L = 2$–7, consistent with table 3.1. It was because the Newtonian force law failed to reproduce the correct physics in the extended regions of spiral galaxies that 'dark' matter was invoked in the first place.

Finally, using the new physics (described in more detail in Chapter 4), I have been able to extend the work to the problem of 'dark' matter in clusters and super-clusters of galaxies as illustrated by the table 3.1, which shows that extremely large M/L ratios have been determined. In fact, it would follow from conventional Newtonian mechanics that most of the mass of large clusters is entirely of the 'dark' variety.[26] But by applying the Carmelian cosmology to clusters of various sizes and comparing with available observational data, I have been able to show that on these scales, also, there is no need to assume the existence of *any* 'dark' matter. This is the subject of my ongoing research, but preliminary calculations indicate it to be true.[27]

The research so far on the anomalous rotation curves of spiral galaxies indicates that the additional speed that the stars and gases attain in the extremities of the disk regions is the result of the gas molecules coupling to the expansion of the fabric of space itself when the forces are very weak. In such regimes, it was discovered that the gravitational force is not proportional to the inverse square of the distance, as we all learnt in high school, but proportional to the inverse distance itself. This is a similar situation to the MOND empirical theory, but in this case there is a rigorous underlying relativistic theory. This leads to the fact that the stars seem to be pushed around the outer disks faster than we would otherwise expect.

However, probably the biggest challenge the new physics is presented with is to explain the dynamics of the hot gas in the intercluster medium that separates the galaxies in the large clusters. Astronomers estimate that the hot x-ray-emitting gas comprises a much greater mass than the actual

NASA and The Hubble Heritage Team (STScI/AURA), ref. 28.

Figure 3.6: A typical spiral galaxy—the beautiful Sombrero (M104) galaxy.

Figure 3.7: A large group of galaxies—the Abell 1689 cluster.

NASA, N. Benítez (JHU), T. Broadhurst (Racah Institute of Physics/ The Hebrew University), H. Ford (JHU), M. Clampin (STScI), G. Hartig (STScI), G. Illingworth (UCO/Lick Observatory), the ACS Science Team and ESA, ref. 29.

galaxies themselves in the clusters, and for the purposes of determining the mass of the clusters, from the thermodynamics of the gas, the galaxies can be ignored. (See fig 3.7 for example.)

The usual analysis is to assume that the x-ray emissions from the gas result from thermal sources and that the potential energy compressing the gas is the result of the total gravitational energy of the system. Hence, by applying the collisionless Boltzmann equation (because 'dark' matter is assumed collisionless), the mass of the gas is calculated once the temperature is measured. The x-ray sources are not assumed to be 'dark' matter, but it is assumed that the compression of the normal (and x-ray-emitting) matter results from the much larger gravitational potential, which comes from a significant proportion of 'dark' matter.

Following the same approach, I was able to determine that the bulk of the heating of the intercluster gas results from the motions of the gas ions and molecules resulting from the expansion of the fabric of space itself. These are also in a very low force regime, which means the orbits of the gases are not according to the usual Newtonian laws but are Carmelian. Under these circumstances, the random motions of the gas particles contribute significantly to the heating, and hence thermodynamics and can be accounted for without invoking 'exotic' dark matter.

The way forward

Using the Carmelian cosmology, 'dark' matter can be eliminated on all scales in the universe. The Carmeli metric more correctly describes the properties of the vacuum, i.e. the expanding space, and this has a measurable effect on the motions of particles in galaxies. Until now, most astrophysicists believed that gravity dominated in galaxies and no effect from Hubble expansion was possible. Furthermore, the Carmeli metric correctly describes the expanding universe, without the need for the invention of 'dark' energy, a cosmological constant or other exotic ideas. The new physics extends the analysis to the dynamics of single galaxies, clusters of galaxies, super-clusters and the whole universe, where the new physics describes the motions without the need for exotic 'dark' matter. These results have the potential to cause another revolution in our understanding of the cosmos. It is akin to the time at the beginning of the last century when Einstein rid the solar system of 'dark' matter.

References

1. The point of closest approach of the planet to the sun.
2. On November 25, nearly ten years after the foundation of special relativity, Einstein submitted his paper 'The Field Equations of Gravitation' for publication. See <www.nobelprize.org/educational_games/physics/relativity/history-1.html>.
3. Wright, A.E. and Disney, M.J., Universal gravity: was Newton right? *Proc. ASA* **8**(4):334–338, 1990.
4. This class of SNe has lent itself very well to this as it was discovered that even though the supernovae represent a distribution of brightness, they can be calibrated to a single standard using the time it takes the light at maximum brightness to die away.
5. Riess, A.G., Filippenko, A.V., Challis, P., Clocchiatti, A. and Diercks, A., Observational evidence from supernovae for an accelerating universe and a cosmological constant, *Astron. J.* **116**(Sept):1009–1038, 1998.
6. Tonry, J., Schmidt, B.P. *et al.*, Cosmological results from high-z supernovae, *Ap. J.* **594** (Sept 1):1–24, 2003.
7. Weakly Interactive Massive Particles.
8. Massive Compact Halo Objects.
9. Carmeli, M., *Classical Fields*, World Scientific, Singapore, 1982.
10. Behar, S. and Carmeli, M., Cosmological relativity: A new theory of cosmology, *Int. J. Theor. Phys.* **39**(5):1375–1396, 2000. Carmeli, M., Cosmological relativity: Determining the universe by the cosmological redshift as infinite and curved, *Int. J. Theor. Phys.* **40**(10):1871–1874, 2001. Carmeli, M., *Cosmological Special Relativity*, 2nd ed. World Scientific, Singapore, 2002.
11. Carmeli, M., Cosmological general relativity, *Communications in Theoretical Physics* **5**:159, 1996.

12. A geometric function that describes the distances between pairs of points in a space.

13. Hartnett, J.G., Carmeli's accelerating universe is spatially flat without dark matter, *Int. J. Theor. Phys.* **44**(4):485–492, <arxiv.org/abs/gr-qc/0407083>, 2005.

14. Hartnett, J.G., The distance modulus determined from Carmeli's cosmology fits the accelerating universe data of the high-redshift type Ia supernovae without dark matter, *Found. Phys.* **36**(6):839–861, June 2006, <arxiv.org/abs/astro-ph/0501526>; Oliveira, F.J. and Hartnett, J.G., Carmeli's cosmology fits data for an accelerating and decelerating universe without dark matter or dark energy, *Found. Phys. Lett.* **19**(6):519–535, November 2006, <arxiv.org/abs/astro-ph/0603500>.

15. Carmeli, M., *Cosmological Special Relativity*, 2nd ed. World Scientific, Singapore, 2002.

16. Carmeli, M., *Cosmological Relativity*, World Scientific, Singapore, 2006.

17. For a good review, see Sofue, Y. and Rubin, V., Rotation curves of spiral galaxies, *Annual Review of Atomic and Molecular Physics* **39**:137–174, 2001.

18. Begeman, K.G., Broeils, A.H. and Sanders R.H., Extended rotation curves of spiral galaxies: Dark haloes and modified dynamics, *M.N.R.A.S.* **249**:523–537, 1991.

19. MOND = MOdified Newtonian Dynamics. See Milgrom, M., A modification of the Newtonian dynamics—Implications for galaxies, *Astrophysical Journal* **270**:371–383, 1983; Milgrom, M., A modification of the Newtonian dynamics—Implications for galaxy systems. *Astrophysical Journal* **270**:384–389, 1983; Milgrom, M., A modification of the Newtonian dynamics as a possible alternative to the hidden mass hypothesis. *Astrophysical Journal* **270**:365–370, 1983.

20. Beckenstein has developed a fully relativistic (TeVeS = Tensor Vector Scalar) theory that incorporates all possible fields. By contrast, Einstein's general relativity theory is a relativistic Tensor field theory. Beckenstein was motivated to generate a theory that would produce MOND without encountering the non-relativistic aspects in conflict with general relativity. See <www.en.wikipedia.org/wiki/Tensor-vector-scalar_gravity>.

21. Disney, M.J., *The Hidden Universe*, Dent, London, 1984.

22. Wright, A.E. and Disney, M.J., Universal gravity: Was Newton right? *Proceedings of the Astronomical Society of Australia* **8**(4):334–338, 1990.

23. Carmeli, M., Derivation of the Tully–Fisher Law: Doubts about the necessity and existence of halo dark matter, *Int. J. Theor. Phys.* **39**(5):1397–1404, 2000; Carmeli, M., Is galaxy dark matter a property of spacetime? *Int. J. Theor. Phys.* **37**(10):2621–2625, 1998.

24. Technically, what astronomers are doing is measuring the rotation speeds of the outermost tracer gases on the edge of the disks of stars. In these regions the rotation curves are usually constant as a function of radial distance, so one can imagine this to be a rotation speed for the whole galaxy.

25. Hartnett, J.G., Spiral galaxy rotation curves determined from Carmelian general relativity, *Int. J. Theor. Phys.* **45**(11): 2118–2136, 2006, <arxiv.org/abs/astro-ph/0511756>.

26. Galaxies in clusters orbit around their common centre of mass. Instead of planetary motion around a central body, the dynamics has, until now, still been considered Newtonian, but in this case, the virial theorem is used to calculate the dynamical masses. That requires a cluster to be in virial equilibrium—a state of dynamic equilibrium. The virial theorem states that, for a stable, self-gravitating distribution of objects (galaxies etc., and indeed gas particles), the time-averaged total kinetic energy of the objects is equal to minus half the time-averaged total potential energy. In galaxies, energy may shift between gravitational potential energy and kinetic energy for the individual objects, but the time-averaged values of the total potential and total kinetic energies of the system remain constant. The constituents will never break up unless acted upon by outside forces. The positions and velocities of the constituents are bounded for all time. It is the analogue of stable planetary orbits.

27. Hartnett, J.G., Spheroidal and elliptical galaxy radial velocity dispersion determined from cosmological general relativity, <arxiv.org/abs/0707.2858>.

28. See <www.hubblesite.org/newscenter/archive/releases/2003/28/image/a>.

29. See <www.hubblesite.org/newscenter/archive/releases/2003/01/image/a>.

Chapter 4:

Einstein and beyond

Chapter 4: Einstein and beyond

When I first saw the words 'Cosmological Special Relativity'—the title of one of Carmeli's books—it really puzzled me, because as a physicist I would not normally expect to see these words used together. Special relativity usually deals with processes that are very non-cosmological in size. It involves itself with the changes in physical dimensions, mass and the flow of time associated with very fast-moving particles and objects. Cosmology, on the other hand, is usually associated with very large-scale processes that we don't normally associate with special relativity. So I was intrigued about the meaning of the words.

Special relativity is really a theory of invariance. That is what Einstein originally wanted to call it. For example, an observer would always determine the same value for the speed of light, no matter what his motion. This value is usually referred to by the letter c, for *constant*, or the Latin word *celeritas*, meaning 'swiftness'. So c is a universal constant, an invariant quantity.

What is always measured in experiments to determine how fast light travels is what we call the two-way speed of light, i.e. measured as it travels to somewhere and back again. It has been described as the limiting constant for all causally related events in the universe and is related to how fast an object or light may travel in the universe. It imposes a speed limit on all forms of propagation.

In the new theory, the parameters that are observed are the relative distances and velocities of the galaxies in the universe. Carmeli theorized that any physical description must relate these quantities in the same way as Einstein did in special relativity. The substance of his universe is therefore called *spacevelocity* instead of *spacetime*.

So he made a substitution, essentially an analogous theory to special relativity, but this time a special relativity for the cosmos. He noted that in 1929 Hubble had discovered that the universe is expanding, and this interpretation of the evidence of redshifts found in starlight has been strengthened ever since. (In chapter 5, I discuss in more detail the observations and interpretations of Hubble and the expanding universe.)

When dealing with distances and velocities in the cosmos, astronomers rely heavily on the meaning of the redshifts they observe in the light they receive in their telescopes from stars and galaxies.

All gases, when heated, emit light at characteristic wavelengths. So the atmospheres of stars emit colours that are characteristic of those gases that they have in their atmospheres. Moreover the ionized atoms in their atmospheres absorb or emit photons of light at very discrete frequencies, which has been well characterized by modern quantum physics. The result is that we see bright (emission) or dark (absorption)

Figure 4.1: Redshift of starlight. The spectrum of the light from a star is compared to a lab sample. Spectral lines identify the gases present in the atmospheres of stars, and this fact makes the comparison possible. The lines then are seen to be either shifted towards the blue end (blueshift) or the red end of the spectrum (redshift).

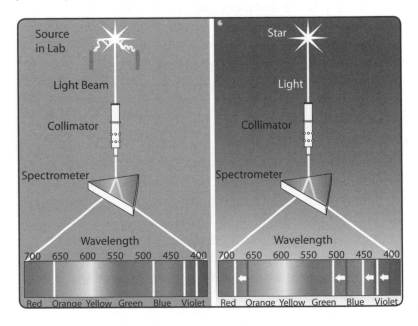

lines in the spectra of stars. This is also true of all sources in the cosmos, including galaxies that are used to determine the 'expansion rate' of the universe.

When spectra are compared to a laboratory sample containing the same gases, as determined by the spectra, it is noted that the lines are shifted either towards the red end of the spectrum or towards the blue end. This is illustrated in fig. 4.1. The interpretation is that the shifting of these spectral lines means the source is in motion. We are seeing the same sort of effect (called the Doppler effect)

Figure 4.2: Police siren changes pitch as it passes because of the Doppler effect.

as occurs when the sound from a police car siren is raised and lowered in pitch as the police car speeds by, as shown in fig. 4.2. This effect is crucial to the interpretation that the universe is expanding.

Initially, astronomers calculated a speed for the extragalactic sources and noted that most were redshifts.[1] Therefore they were rushing away from us. Nowadays, this interpretation has been replaced by cosmological expansion of the fabric of space and the idea that the galaxies are not moving through space but that the space is expanding, or stretching, and the galaxies are going along for the ride, so to speak. So the redshifts can then be interpreted as a velocity of the expansion. It is not that the galaxies actually move through space, but that the space expands. This idea is crucial to the standard FL models and is quantified by the Hubble Law.

The Hubble Law simply relates the velocity (v) of the expansion to the distance (r) of the source, by the simple formula

$$v = H_0\, r \qquad (4.1)$$

where H_0 is a constant of proportionality called the Hubble constant. The law then can be read as saying that *the greater the distance, the greater the velocity.*

Carmeli then made the assertion that this law (4.1) is fundamental to all observers in the universe, but rewritten in the following form:

$$v = \left(\frac{1}{\tau}\right) r \qquad (4.2)$$

where τ, the Carmeli–Hubble time constant, is a universal constant and the same for all observers, regardless of epoch, which means regardless of *when* the measurement is made. The idea is supported by the fact that the measurement of H_0 has been very difficult and the value varies widely depending on the method used, yet it has emerged that there is an inherent scale dependence to its value. That means that depending on the distances to the sources that were used to determine the value of H_0, one would get a different result. Hence it is not constant, whereas Carmeli's constant (τ) is truly constant.

In the past,[2] I have challenged the trustworthiness of the Hubble Law (4.1). However, when measurements are based on the redshifts of the large central elliptical and the brightest spiral galaxies of a cluster, the

Hubble Law has applicability. It has been shown by Hubble, and later by Sandage, that these galaxies do indeed follow the Hubble Law. Even if the distance to the galaxies is somewhat in doubt, the relationship holds for their apparent magnitude (brightness).

This can be understood in terms of the redshifts of a class of galaxies. If the brightest galaxy of a cluster is selected from many different clusters, then it is a fair assumption that they will all have approximately the same intrinsic size, hence the same absolute brightness.[3] This is like selecting the tallest person from different random groups of people. Those people selected will have approximately the same height.[4] (See Appendix 5.)

Consequently, using reliable Hubble 'constant' data as a function of redshift, even though there are large measurement errors, the Carmeli–Hubble time constant has been evaluated at $\tau \approx 13.5$ billion years. (See section 4 of Appendix 2.)

The constant τ is the reciprocal of the Hubble constant (H_0) in the limit of weak gravity. It is a characteristic time constant and not the age of the universe. When we use the expression 'age of the universe', to be correct we need to specify *by which clocks*.

Also what one must understand here—picture in your mind—is that we are talking about a new dimension to the universe. It is not a dimension in the sense of length, breadth and depth, but a real dimension nevertheless. It is a *velocity dimension* and is illustrated in fig. 4.3, where we see that, as the universe expands, the galaxies are not moving through space, but the fabric of space itself is expanding with the velocity (v).

The analogy to special relativity is complete with the replacement of the *time* dimension with a *velocity* dimension and the universal constant c with a new universal constant τ. And similarly to Einstein with his special relativity theory, Carmeli initially developed his CSR theory without assuming the existence of any matter in the universe.

After including matter, his cosmological *general* relativity (CGR) theory emerged. The new theory is

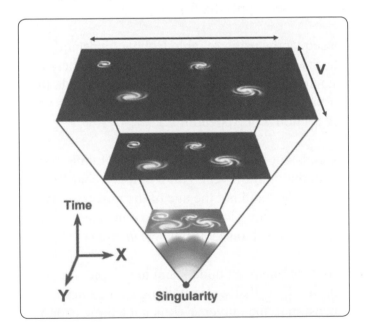

Figure 4.3: Expanding space shown as a function of time. The fabric of space is stretched with velocity (v) the new dimension, ref. 5.

elegant in that it is simple. It describes the motion of galaxies in the expanding *observable* universe. Only the Hubble–Carmeli time constant (τ), the present epoch average mass density (Ω) and the familiar, well-known constants are needed.

CGR assumes a spherically symmetric universe with the observer at the centre. The galaxies are distributed accordingly and we observe redshifts so the universe is expanding. The theory only assumes isotropy and not homogeneity. (This assumption is dealt with in Chapter 5.)

CGR describes three phases of the universal expansion, initially decelerating, then passing through a constant or coasting phase (where the pressure is zero) to an accelerating phase (where the pressure is positive). When the universe was dense it expanded with a decelerating expansion eventually reaching the coasting stage, when the matter density reached the critical density[6] (about 10^{-29} g.cm^{-3}). Eventually it accelerated to the state it is in today, where the average matter density is well below the critical value. The tri-phase expansion of his model is testable and has been successfully applied to the observational brightness-distance data of type Ia supernovae, collected by astronomers since 1997.

Challenging the big bang

Carmeli's model is a challenge to standard big bang theory, because it shows that a model other than the standard FL models can describe the largest-scale structure of the universe without two of the vitally needed add-ons, 'dark' matter and 'dark' energy.

CGR really is a description of the structure of the visible universe, taking into account what we *can,* rather than *cannot,* observe. Its strength lies in its simplicity. Just as it offers a solution to the dynamics of galaxies in the universe without requiring the assumption of 'dark' matter or 'dark' energy, it may also offer solutions to some other puzzling questions that astronomers and physicists have yet to solve.

Einstein's field equations

In 1915, though preceded by many other contributors, Albert Einstein found the correct field equations that describe the structure of the cosmos.

$$G_{\mu v} = R_{\mu v} - \tfrac{1}{2} R = \kappa T_{\mu v} \qquad (4.3)$$

These are the equations that relate how *spacetime* is affected or curved by the presence of matter and energy. In relativity, gravitation is no longer a force but the result of geometry and curvature, represented by $G_{\mu v}$, the Einstein tensor in (4.3).[7] It is, in effect, the stage on which the drama of the universe is played out. And the curvature is related to the matter and energy content of the universe represented by the parameter $T_{\mu v}$ the energy/momentum tensor. The number κ couples these quantities from each side of equation (4.3).

The total amount of matter and energy in the universe (expressed as a fraction of the amount necessary for the universe to reach the coasting stage, but not quite enough that gravity wins and it collapses back on itself) is the critical density. Matter density is usually represented by the symbol Ω. In (4.3) the energy/ momentum tensor $T_{\mu\nu}$ is a function of density Ω.

In FL models, the value of Ω determines the future of the universe. If $\Omega < 1$, then the universe is open and space has a hyperbolic geometry; if $\Omega > 1$, the universe is closed and space has an elliptical geometry. If $\Omega = 1$, then the universe is geometrically flat; i.e. it has the Euclidean geometry that we experience locally. The curvature is determined by the total mass/energy density Ω, which includes all matter (both normal and 'dark') and 'dark' energy. Nowadays in FL models the total mass/energy density is constrained to unity, meaning the sum of all matter and all energy gives the universe a density just equal to the critical density. Therefore it follows that the universe is open and space is flat, i.e. Euclidean.

Einstein formulated his equations in the four dimensions of space (3) and time (1). His general theory has since been thoroughly tested on Earth, in space and in the solar system. As mentioned in chapter 2, it solved a long-standing problem, that of the advance of the perihelion of the planet Mercury. Carmeli found that Einstein's field equations were also valid in his new *spacevelocity*, four dimensions of space (3) and velocity (1). Carmeli solved them for the expanding universe. Later he added back the time dimension when dealing with dynamics on length scales smaller than the whole universe. This resulted in a five-dimensional theory.

The new *spacevelocity,* however, differed from Einstein's *spacetime* by one important point. Carmeli posited that the universe is never empty of matter—a valid assumption it seems. Therefore, in his new theory, he envisaged a new quantity called *effective matter density* (equal to $\Omega - 1$), which could equal zero, even become negative (if $\Omega < 1$), which normal matter density Ω can never do. This meant that space had a property that caused it to expand—something like a compressed spring, which, when released, would expand rapidly. The universe started initially with a very high value of this *effective matter density* ($\Omega - 1$) and as this expanded it has been reducing ever since, passing through zero and becoming ever more negative.

Since *the physics is in the geometry,* which is determined in part by the matter density, the theory is somewhat different from FL models, as Ω now describes the geometry of *spacevelocity,* not only *spacetime.* Since the measured matter density Ω is less than unity, the universe is open, and it means, in the Carmeli theory, an accelerating universe which will expand forever, never collapsing back on itself. However, the Carmeli theory does not need to invent 'dark' matter and 'dark' energy.

The theory also indicates that the universe is spatially flat, which is consistent with our experience. And it has always been flat. This is where it also differs, as the FL models would need the mass/energy density equal to the critical density ($\Omega = 1$). The new theory *does not* specifically incorporate a cosmological constant (Λ) as the FL theorists are required to do; however, an equivalent cosmological constant can be determined from the model. It turns out to be non-zero and positive, extremely small and the right magnitude.

But don't be mistaken; though Carmeli is some sort of a rebel in that he has challenged the established thinking, in his mind his new theory does not present as anything more than a new type of big bang model. However, we can apply the same theory to extract a new model that is consistent with what we would expect, starting with the Genesis history. The starting conditions cannot be determined from observations, and even if we could see back in time to the beginning, the same data could support a range of different historical interpretations—there is no unique history presented by the evidence.

Evidence: High-redshift supernova observations

In order to test these cosmological theories against the large-scale structure of the universe, an independent method of determining distance in the universe needed to be found. The method used nowadays is to establish a 'standard candle' and use the inverse square law of illumination. The more distant the source, the dimmer it becomes. All one needs to do is determine how intrinsically bright the 'standard candle' is. The discovery of the type Ia supernova allowed astrophysicists to measure both the distance to a candidate source galaxy, which is the host to the exploding star, and obtain a redshift measurement of the light from this host galaxy, which would give the recession speed. It was found that type Ia supernovae can be calibrated to a standard, even though they had different light curves. The light curve is the brightening function of the supernova as a function of time. It was discovered that the brighter the supernova, the longer the time for the light to decay away.

When the FL models were tested[9] in this way, it was found that the theory would only fit the observed data when large quantities of 'dark' matter and 'dark' energy were added to the mix. The best-fit FL model requires the total matter density of the universe to be

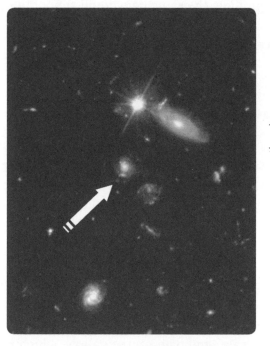

NASA and J. Blakeslee (JHU), ref.8

Figure 4.4: Hubble Space Telescope image of type Ia supernova SN 2002dd. Arrow indicates the light near the host galaxy that wasn't seen in earlier images of the galaxy.

about 26% (or $\Omega = 0.26$) but when the matter density Ω is measured locally, we get somewhere between 0.7% and 4.1%.[10] This amount, even if we assume the high end of the range ($\Omega = 0.04$), is not enough to fit the observed expansion when using the high-redshift supernova data. Hence, the assumption that the discrepancy must be due to 'dark' matter.

But even this was not enough. From the SNe Ia observations, it appeared that the 'standard candles' are still dimmer than they should be—hence, something else must be driving the universe apart. This led to the idea that the universe is accelerating—pushed by an unseen force, the alleged 'dark' energy. By reinserting the cosmological constant (Λ) into the left-hand side of Einstein's field equations (4.3), it can explain these observations, even though its numerical value is extremely small. Some thought of more exotic causes for the 'dark' energy—quintessence, for example, a slowly evolving scalar field—but these have all but been ruled out by recent surveys. From this resulted the division of matter and energy as shown in fig. 3.3 with a total (including 'dark') matter density $\Omega = 0.26$ and a 'dark' energy density $\Omega_\Lambda = 0.74$, hence $\Omega + \Omega_\Lambda = 1$.

When the Carmelian *spacevelocity* theory is applied to the same observational data (see Appendix 2) the fit is incredibly good without the need to invoke either 'dark' matter or 'dark' energy. The fit to the data is performed with essentially one free parameter, the matter density of the universe, and the best fit value is determined to be $\Omega = 0.04 \pm 0.02$. This result is totally consistent with the measured normal-matter density from luminous sources. The quality of the fit (theory to data) is also extremely good. It indicates that it follows from the Carmelian theory that the universe must be of very low matter density. This confirms Carmeli's original belief that $\Omega < 1$ and hence that the universe is accelerating.

So the new theory, when tested against this evidence, performs well without the need for 'fudge factors'.[11] Since the theory explains SNe Ia data, the question must be asked as to whether it can explain other observations in the cosmos. This will be explored in subsequent chapters.

The Carmelian theory is inherently a description of a spherically symmetric low-matter-density universe. It assumes that the Hubble Law is the underlying principle by which galaxies are distributed throughout the universe, with the observer at the centre of the expansion. But is the observer uniquely at the centre? And what does the new theory tell us about the size of the universe? And how is matter distributed throughout?

References

1. See <www.en.wikipedia.org/wiki/Vesto_Slipher>.
2. Hartnett, J.G., Quantized quasar redshifts in a creationist cosmology, *J. of Creation* **18**(2):105–113, 2004; Hartnett, J.G., The heavens declare a different story! *J. of Creation* **17**(2):94–97, 2003.
3. See from fig. 4 of Sandage, A., The redshift–distance relation II. The Hubble diagram and its scatter for first-ranked cluster galaxies: a formal value for q_0, *Ap. J.* **178**(Nov 15):1–24, 1972, which has been reproduced in Hartnett, J.G., Quantized quasar redshifts in a creationist cosmology, *J. of Creation* **18**(2):105–113, 2004. In the figure, the ordinate axis is the logarithmic redshift of a galaxy and the co-ordinate axis is its corrected visual magnitude. Apparent magnitude is a measure of distance, according to the inverse square law of illumination.
4. Astronomers must be careful in choosing the appropriate clusters. For example, according to Arp (*Seeing Red*, pp. 153 & 154), galaxy clusters in the Abell catalogue have a notoriously large scatter about the Hubble line in a redshift-magnitude plot. Arp has noted this effect in many clusters that indicate some disturbed or active character, like the Abell clusters that are strong X-ray sources.
5. See <www.en.wikipedia.org/wiki/Image:Universe_expansion.png>.
6. This is in fact the definition of 'critical' density.
7. The details of the curvature are described by $R_{\mu\nu}$ and R, the Ricci tensor and the Ricci scalar.
8. See <hubblesite.org/newscenter/archive/releases/2003/12/image/c>.
9. Knop, R.A. *et al.*, 'New constraints on Ω_M, Ω_Λ and ω from an independent set of 11 high-redshift supernovae observed with the Hubble Space Telescope', *Ap. J.* **598**:102–137, 2003; Riess, A.G. *et al.*, 'Type Ia supernovae discoveries at $z > 1$ from the Hubble Space Telescope: Evidence for past deceleration and constraints on dark energy evolution', *Ap. J.* **607**:665–687, 2004; Astier, P. *et al.*, 'The Supernova Legacy Survey: Measurement of Ω_M, Ω_Λ and ω from the first year data set', A & A 447:31–48, 2006.
10. Fukugita, M., Hogan, C.J. and Peebles, P.J.E., The cosmic baryon budget, *Ap. J.* **503**:518–530, 1998.
11. Of course there are other competing non-FL theories that also explain the same data.

Chapter 5:

Our galaxy—at the centre of the action

Chapter 5: Our galaxy—at the centre of the action

The Bible makes it plain that mankind is the focus of God's attention, and that the universe was specially created by God for His glory—which implies that it was made for us to see. It is a reasonable assumption then that He placed Earth in the centre of His universe so we would see how great He is. That is, we are likely at or very near the centre of the universe filled with billions of galaxies with billions of stars in each one. This is what Edwin Hubble initially concluded. His observations of galaxy redshifts indicated to him that we are at the centre of a spherically symmetric distribution of galaxies. But Hubble subsequently rejected his own conclusion—i.e. that we are in a very special place—on philosophical grounds. He wrote:

> 'Such a condition would imply that we occupy *a unique position in the universe* … . But the unwelcome supposition of a favoured location must be avoided at all costs … . Such a *favoured position*, of course, is *intolerable*; moreover, it represents a discrepancy with the theory, because the theory postulates homogeneity [emphasis added].'[1]

What prompted these comments was that he was seeing galaxies *in all directions* speeding away from him in proportion to their distance. According to his interpretation of those redshifts, he concluded that the more distant the galaxy, the faster it moved. This meant we must be at the centre of the universe—but Hubble rejected that idea. He went on to say:

'Therefore, in order to restore homogeneity, and to escape *the horror of a unique position*, the departures from uniformity, which are introduced by the recession factors, must be compensated by the second term representing the effects of spatial curvature [emphasis added].'[2]

But there is more to it. The observations that brought Hubble to that point were redshifts. He, and others, observed the redshift of the spectral lines in light from very distant sources. It appeared that the galaxies we see were rapidly receding and their redshifts were the result of a Doppler effect. Nowadays cosmologists consider not that the galaxies are moving, but that *space itself* is moving (or expanding) and the galaxies are fixed to (or stationary in) space.

Hubble was thus concerned that *interpreting the redshifts as recession* of the galaxies would introduce a further problem, in that the 'numbers of [galaxies] increase faster than the volume of space through which they are scattered'.[3] This new problem could only be solved *by assuming that space was curved. If curved, then a centre could be avoided. There would then be no need for a centre or an edge to the universe; hence we would not be in a unique position.* Hubble continues:

'Relativity contributes the basic proposition that geometry of space is determined by the contents of space. To this principle has been added another proposition, formulated in various ways and called by various names, but equivalent, in a sense, to the statement that all observers, regardless of location, will see the same general picture of the universe. *The second principle is a sheer assumption.* It seems plausible and it appeals strongly to our sense of proportion. Nevertheless, it leads to a remarkable consequence, for it demands that, if we see the [galaxies] all receding from our position in space, then every other observer, no matter where he may be located, will see the [galaxies] all receding from his position. *However, the assumption is adopted. There must be no favoured location in the universe, no centre, no boundary; all must see the universe alike* [emphasis added].'[4]

The assumption here is called by names like the Copernican or the cosmological principle, but it basically says that, on the largest scales, the universe, or the distribution of galaxies in it, is homogeneous. That means that any observer anywhere in the universe would always see the same 'big picture' of the heavens.

Richard Feynman succinctly describes the problem of the cosmological principle:

'... I suspect that the assumption of uniformity of the universe reflects a prejudice born of a sequence of overthrows of geocentric ideas ... . It would be embarrassing to find, after stating that we live in an ordinary planet about an ordinary star in an ordinary galaxy, that our place in the universe is extraordinary ... . To avoid embarrassment we cling to the hypothesis of uniformity.'[5]

However, given the focus of God on humanity, it is a reasonable assumption that the universe is both finite (though extremely large) *and* bounded. There are two points to consider here. On one hand, the idea of uniformity suggests the universe has no unique centre and, hence, no edge. On the other hand, if we accept that the universe is finite in size *and* we reject the notion of uniformity, based on either observations and/or prior assumptions, then we must conclude that the universe is bounded.

So, does the Bible give any clues? The psalmist said:

'He determines *the number* of the stars and calls them *each by name*' (Psalms 147:4) [emphasis added].

And as God told Abraham:

'I will surely bless you and make your descendants as numerous as the stars in the sky and *as the sand on the seashore*' (Genesis 22:17) [emphasis added].

Though I can't 'prove' it from the Bible, it is a reasonable assumption that, like the grains of the sand by the seashore, the number of stars is, though unimaginably large, still *finite*. Only God Himself is infinite. It makes sense that the universe would also be bounded. Consider reaching a point where space comes to an end—the idea that there is something beyond that, something 'outside of' the universe of matter/energy/space, makes a great deal of sense biblically. God existed before His creation—He is separate from it, 'outside' of it (though immanent in it). If the universe is *also bounded,*[6] then it must also have a unique centre and an edge. This would then destroy the idea of homogeneity, as an observer near the edge would have a very different view of the universe.

But this idea of something 'outside' of the universe would be anathema to those who reject the Lord. It's little wonder that today there is so much insistence on unbounded models in cosmology. The cosmological principle may be restated as saying that there is nothing special about our location in the universe, and it absolutely requires that there be no centre and no edge. This 'no centre and no edge' idea provides for an easy solution for Einstein's field equations (4.3) for the cosmos. This is how Friedmann, in 1922, and Lemaître, in 1927, reasoned. If we were to discover that we are in a privileged location in the universe, then it would naturally follow that we are part of a special creation. Clearly Hubble accepted this line of reasoning. But I contend that the evidence (including some recent observational evidence we will discuss shortly) is consistent with God's Word and is better interpreted according to the finite, bounded worldview.[7]

The creationist model I present here involves a bounded distribution of galaxies, centred on our galaxy. This alters the boundary conditions that we need to apply to our mathematical modelling; it also raises questions about what differences regarding the observations of distant sources we expect to see in our universe. For example, what sorts of redshifts would we see in such a universe? I will attempt to answer such questions. (See Appendix 4 for details.)

Today, as in Hubble's time, observations can still be interpreted as indicating that we are at the centre of a spherical matter distribution. George Ellis, the cosmologist and politician from South Africa, was quoted in *Scientific American*:

> "'People need to be aware that there is a range of models that could explain the observations,'" Ellis argues. "For instance, I can construct you a spherically symmetrical universe with Earth at its center, and you cannot disprove it based on observations." Ellis has published a paper on this. "You can only exclude it on philosophical grounds. In my view there is absolutely nothing wrong in that. What I want to bring into the open is the fact that we are using philosophical criteria in choosing our models. A lot of cosmology tries to hide that.'"[8]

The only thing, he is saying, that can make the distinction is your worldview. Scientific facts can't help there. A further question, then, assuming a spherically symmetric distribution of matter, is: how large is it, and is there an edge?

If the universe is infinite and matter extends in all directions forever, we call this unbounded and infinite. Such a universe could be spherically symmetrically

Figure 5.1: Ball of matter—spherically symmetric matter distribution

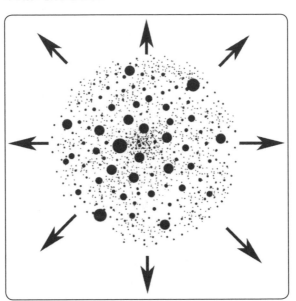

centred on Earth, but extend to infinity, provided the matter was isotropically distributed around us. This means that in every direction we look, we see the same distribution as a function of distance. Compare this with the layers of an onion. From the centre, the layers are isotropic yet not homogeneous. If one were to move from the centre, the isotropy would be lost.

If the universe is finite, then there are two possibilities. For a finite spherically symmetric universe, we could either have what we are familiar with, like a ball of dust, with a centre and an edge (fig. 5.1), which we call 'finite' and 'bounded' or we could have a finite unbounded universe. However, the finite unbounded version (the most popular amongst

Figure 5.2: Big bang hypersphere. The surface of the balloon is a 2D analogy for the 3D space containing galaxies in the universe. As the balloon expands, the pictured galaxies all move away from each other. There is no unique centre. For the analogy to work, the 3D space must be curved into an additional dimension—hyperspace.

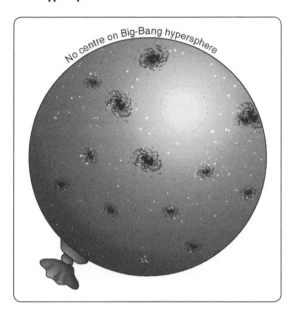

No centre on Big-Bang hypersphere

big bangers, at least until relatively recently) requires homogeneity. The closed version of this is illustrated in fig. 5.2.

A spherical distribution of matter of finite extent (a ball of dust, see fig. 5.1) will have a special point towards which there is a net gravitational force. That is the centre of the ball if it is evenly spread out in all directions (i.e. isotropic). This type of universe is finite and has an edge. The centre can be likened to the centre of a depression inside a circular ring of hills. The gravitational potential—the energy stored in the gravitational field—then becomes a significant concept. This is the approach that Humphreys took. However in the Carmeli model it turns out that because space is always locally flat there is no gravitational effects observable in the universe. The reason is because the new physics introduces a new dimension, which takes the place of *spacetime* 'curvature' in general relativity. (See Appendix 4.)

In the FL models, which insist on a homogeneous universe, there is no centre—or, alternatively, it could be said that the centre is everywhere. There is no significant gravitational potential provided the matter in the universe is evenly and uniformly distributed; this energy is not considered to produce any special effects. In FL models, by definition, over the largest scales, there can be no gravitational potential differences from place to place. This is a result of the homogeneity assumption. And note that a homogeneous universe must also be isotropic.

Hubble made many assumptions in 1937 and these assumptions still remain. They are required to avoid the unwelcome (for many) conclusion that the universe is the product of special creation.

Large maps of galaxy distributions

What do we observe in the universe? Do we see a homogeneous distribution of matter? This is a very difficult question to answer, because the usual method of measuring the distances to large collections of very distant galaxies relies on the Hubble Law. But the exact form of the Hubble Law at high redshift (i.e. large distances) depends heavily on the particular details of the assumed cosmological model.

Nevertheless, there have been a couple of large-scale mapping projects that take a slice of the heavens and project it onto a plane. These projects use the Hubble Law and the brightness of the galaxies to create a map. The 2dF Galaxy Redshift Survey (2dFGRS),[9] a joint UK–Australian project, sampled about two hundred thousand galaxies in 2 degree slices above and below the plane of the Galaxy. Fig. 5.3 shows a map of the measured galaxies as a function of distance from the apex, which represents the observer on Earth. Another, the Sloan Digital Sky Survey (SDSS),[10] in 2003 announced the first measurements of galactic structures more than a billion light-years across and mapped about two hundred thousand galaxies in 6% of the sky. A portion of these are shown in fig. 5.4 projected onto a plane. Now more than six hundred thousand have been mapped.

It would appear from these maps that the assumption of homogeneity cannot be supported. These maps are sliced in the plane of the Earth's equator and look like two slices of pizza. Both sections of the 2dFGRS map are shown in fig. 5.3, but only half of the SDSS map in fig. 5.4. The small dots, each representing a galaxy, appear to form into enormous concentric structures centred on the middle (or the tip of the 'pizza slice'), where our galaxy is located. Fig. 5.4 and the left side of fig. 5.3 show not only concentric but also circular structures centred on our galaxy more clearly than do earlier maps. This result is more

Figure 5.3: 2dF Galaxy Redshift Survey (2dFGRS) map: each point showing the position of galaxies with respect to Earth at the apex. The 2dFGRS obtained spectra for 245,591 objects, mainly galaxies, brighter than a nominal extinction-corrected magnitude limit of b_J =19.45. Reliable redshifts were obtained for 221,414 galaxies.

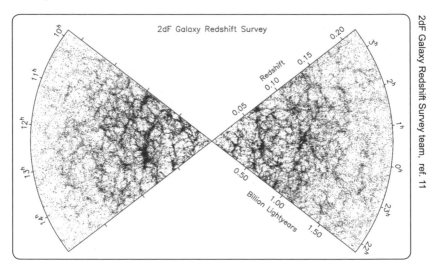

2dF Galaxy Redshift Survey team, ref. 11

than an artefact of the sampling technique because the density distribution of galaxies is expected to increase with distance in a big bang universe, as one looks back in time, until an expected decrease in number is observed due to the fact that the galaxies get too dim to be seen. In these maps, the galaxy density seems to oscillate (decrease and increase periodically) with distance, hence the circular structures.

This spatial galaxy density variation therefore result from the fact that galaxies are preferentially found at certain discrete distances. This means we are located at the centre of concentric great spherical shells, on which the galaxies are located, that seem to be equally spaced with a separation of about one hundred million light-years. This is not likely to be a coincidence—but rather, the result of deliberate design. (See Appendix 5 for a detailed analysis.)

Many assumptions have gone into the construction of these maps, and I would not necessarily agree that they are all justified. However, this evidence is showing, on a very broad scale, something that some have believed for a long time. If these maps are correct, they indicate that *the universe is isotropic but not homogeneous.* Therefore the evidence would seem to indicate that the cosmological principle is wrong. That means that the universe has a unique centre. And we are somewhere near that centre.

Solution to Einstein's field equations

Einstein himself found a static solution to his field equations (4.3), which describe the motion of particles through *spacetime.* He realized that the cosmos was unstable against gravitational collapse, and added a constant to his equations—the cosmological constant (Λ)—to maintain the galaxies in their positions. As soon as he heard of Hubble's findings that the galaxies were receding, Einstein is reported to have said that it had been his life's biggest blunder.

Nowadays the FL solutions of Einstein's field equations provide the usual basis upon which the redshifts of extragalactic objects are understood in the standard big-bang, inflationary cosmologies.

Astrophysical Research Consortium (ARC) and the Sloan Digital Sky Survey (SDSS) Collaboration, <www.sdss.org>, ref. 12

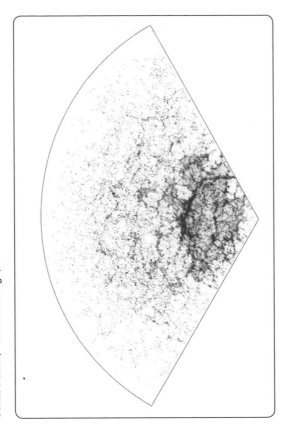

Figure 5.4: Sloan Digital Sky Survey (SDSS) map: each point showing the position of galaxies with respect to Earth at the apex. Their distances were determined from their spectrum to create a 2 billion light-year-deep 3D map where each galaxy is shown as a single point, the colour representing the luminosity. This is the top map of two halves which together show 66,976 that lie near the plane of Earth's equator from the total of 205,443 galaxies mapped.

Carmeli offered a new approach and also solved Einstein's field equations. His universe is described by a metric that is spherically symmetric and isotropic but not necessarily homogeneous. The isotropic galaxy distributions as seen in figs 5.3 and 5.4 are consistent with his theory. But they are not a suitable basis for the FL models. Nevertheless, FL theorists have tried retaining the FL solution, in light of the observed vast voids and long filaments of galaxy clusters seen in these maps, by taking the non-homogeneity into account, as a perturbation on the original models.

The universe Carmeli describes in his book and published papers could be either infinite or finite, yet *unbounded*. He discards the crucial solution—the one that involves a central gravitational potential. In this solution, the universe is bounded (has a unique centre).

However, I have extended the analysis of Carmeli and have found that the solution he arrives at of Einstein's field equations is also valid in a finite bounded universe with a unique centre and edge.[13] It is also consistent with the high redshift type Ia supernova measurements. All that is required is that the physical radius of the universe be equal to the visible radius or greater (i.e. $> c\tau$). (See Appendix 4 for details.) The choice of cosmology, then, is ultimately personal preference, not a requirement dictated by the data.

Figure 5.5: Our galaxy sits at the top of a potential hill, with the rest of the galaxies spherically distributed around it. (Schematic only and not to scale.)

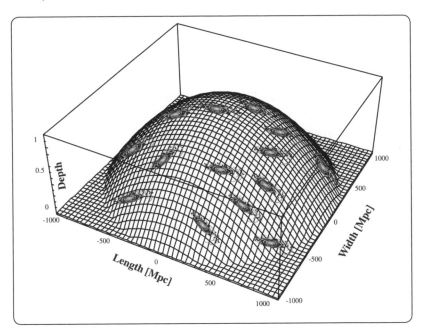

And the solution of Einstein's field equations also indicates that the universe can be best described as not a potential well like that shown in fig. 2.1 but a potential hill as shown in fig. 5.5. Because the universe has expanded over time, the hill was initially large but decreased very rapidly. Another way of describing it is as an expanding white hole with the Galaxy at the centre. A white hole is effectively a black hole but all matter and energy are pouring out—not in. And if the universe is finite as suggested above, then the event horizon is still a long way from us. So we can describe the universe as an expanding white hole with the Galaxy at its centre.

References

1. Hubble, E., *The observational approach to cosmology*, The Clarendon Press, Oxford, pp. 50–59, 1937.
2. Ref. 1, p. 59.
3. Ref. 1, p. 58.
4. Ref. 1, p. 54.
5. Feynman, R.P., Morinigo, F.B. and Wagner, W.G., *Feynman lectures on gravitation*, Penguin Books, London, p. 166, 1999.
6. In cosmology, a finite unbounded universe has no centre and no edge. This can be visualized as the surface of a sphere—the surface representing the three dimensional space that the galaxies occupy.
7. Those who believe in scientific naturalism generally cite a series of developments in human understanding of the universe as pointing inexorably in the direction of 'no special place' for the earth—the Copernican revolution (i.e. the earth is not the centre of the solar system), the finding that the sun revolves around the galaxy, that our galaxy is a member of a relatively small group moving under the gravitational influence of a much larger group, etc.
8. Gibbs, W.W., Profile: George F.R. Ellis; thinking globally, acting universally, *Scientific American* **273**(4):28–29, 1995.
9. See <www.aao.gov.au/2df/>.
10. See <www.sdss.org/>.
11. See <www2.aao.gov.au/2dFGRS>.
12. For a more detailed and complete map, where luminosity is represented by colour, see <www.sdss.org/news/releases/galaxy_zoom.jpg>.
13. Hartnett, J.G., A finite bounded expanding white hole universe without dark matter, <arxiv.org/abs/astro-ph/0508367> 2006.

Chapter 6:

Stretched out the heavens

Chapter 6: Stretched out the heavens

A re the galaxies receding from us because they are moving through space? Or are the galaxies fixed in space and the space is being, or has been, spread out, stretched or expanded, giving the illusion that the galaxies are actually moving? Experimentally and observationally, there is absolutely no way to tell the difference. Redshift, after all, is the measurement of the relative shift in spectral lines determined from a photographic plate or a CCD[1] image. The effect, though, is the same; namely that the distances between us (the 'observer') and the extragalactic sources, which include galaxies and quasars, have rapidly increased at some time in the past.

However, the Bible gives us a clue. Numerous times God says He stretched out the heavens:

'He wraps himself in light as with a garment; he *stretches* out the heavens *like a tent*' (Psalms 104:2).

'He sits enthroned above the circle of the earth, and its people are like grasshoppers. He *stretches* out the heavens like a canopy, and spreads them out *like a tent* to live in' (Isaiah 40:22).

'This is what God the LORD says—he who created the heavens and *stretched* them out, who spread out the earth and all that comes out of it, who gives breath to its people, and life to those who walk on it' (Isaiah 42:5).

'This is what the LORD says—your Redeemer, who formed you in the womb: I am the LORD, who has made all things, who alone *stretched* out the heavens' (Isaiah 44:24).

If we take this as the underlying mechanism for the expansion of the cosmos, then it is more probable that the space has been stretched out and that God did it for a purpose. This was suggested by Russ Humphreys[2] over ten years ago. The stretching of the heavens may have had a specific purpose in God's perfect plan. For example, it could have helped to protect the fledging earth, with its life, from all the initial radiation of the stars in the universe.[3] Massive stretching would cause the intensity of radiation to be reduced—or have some other purpose, as we will see in Chapter 7. But to see where this fits in, let's first summarize some of the important details of the creationary model I propose.

Creation Days 1 to 4

On Day 1, God formed the earth initially from only water—H_2O. There was much more water mass there originally than today. The Word tells us that:

'Now the earth was formless and empty, darkness was over the surface of the deep, and the Spirit of God was hovering over the waters' (Gen 1:2).

At some point, God energized the creation—creating *gravitation* and *electromagnetic energy*, which includes light. This then led to the formless mass of water forming into a sphere under its own gravitation. Next the text tells us:

> 'And God said, "Let there be light," and there was light' (Gen 1:3).

God provided light until He created the sun on Day 4. The light separated a dark side of the rotating earth sphere from the light side. Twenty-four-hour days were determined by the rotation.

On Day 2, God separated the waters. I propose this could mean placing a shell of water in the outer regions of the solar system, to protect the earth and later its inhabitants. Because there was much more water in the original sphere than there is today on Earth, much of it may be found in outer solar system objects. On Day 4, some of this was formed into the gas giants (planets) and Trans-Neptunian objects (sometimes called 'Kuiper Belt Objects', which is a less objective name). Much remains today as icy comets. A lot of 'water' is still out there in a halo around the solar system. Also, a lot of evidence is coming in that the objects (planetoids, comets, etc.) beyond Neptune are largely water ice.[4] This 'water' may also serve to rain down in God's judgment on the ungodly in the Day of our Lord.[5]

On Day 3, God separated the land and water, formed oceans, etc. We mostly see water in the oceans, but we are also told that the rocky crust contains a lot of water.[6]

On Day 4, God created the lights to rule the day (the sun) and night (the moon). He also created the stars. He created the Milky Way galaxy and other large elliptical and spiral galaxies. God stretched out space, by some enormous factor, and spread out the parent galaxies that He then caused to eject more galaxies as quasars in ongoing creation episodes during the course of Day 4.[7]

Galaxy creation

One of the consequences of the Carmelian cosmology is that, as a natural consequence of the conservation of energy, particle production must occur. That is, matter is generated from the vacuum. This is not creation *ex nihilo* but a conversion of one form of energy into another. The only proviso is that the expansion of the universe must not be isentropic— meaning that entropy must not be conserved. Non-conservation of entropy means that as the universe expands, the whole system tends to a state of greater randomness.

This is evident in active galaxies like the galaxy 0313-192, as shown in fig. 6.1, and others like M82[8] and M87.[9] There, radio jets are seen emerging from the active nucleus of the galaxy. This type of thing is not so commonly seen as visible jets but more in the radio part of the spectrum (viewed with radio telescopes) and clearly such signs are obvious manifestations of violent activity inside the compact nuclei of galaxies.

Figure 6.1: The active galaxy 0313-192 ejecting large quantities of material seen as composite images in visible light as well as radio emission. It was the first spiral galaxy known to be producing a giant radio-emitting jet. The upper image shows a wide view of 0313-192 and its surroundings, as seen with the Advanced Camera for Surveys of the NASA Hubble Space Telescope (HST). The radio-emitting jet, as seen with the Very Large Array (VLA)[10] at a wavelength of 20 centimetres, is overlaid in red on the colour image. The galaxy is seen edge-on. The lower image is a close-up of the HST image, with another red overlay from a higher-resolution, 3-centimetre VLA image, showing the inner portion of the jet.

NASA, W. Keel (University of Alabama), M. Ledlow (Gemini Observatory), F. Owen (NRAO) and AUI/NSF, ref. 11.

Now Hubble's Law has been extrapolated to objects, the distance of which cannot be measured by other means, including 'quasars' which, because of their very large redshifts, are considered to be *extremely distant*, out near the edge of the visible universe. The quasars then make up most of the most distant objects of the universe according to standard big bang thinking, because most of the high redshift objects are quasars.

Figure 6.2: A quasar is shown to be embedded and near to the centre of a nearby active spiral galaxy NGC 7319. The arrow indicates the quasar moving towards the observer entraining gas behind it.

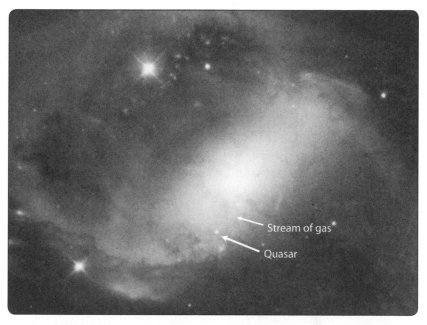

NASA, Jayanne English (University of Manitoba), Sally Hunsberger (Pennsylvania State University), Zolt Levay (Space Telescope Science Institute), Sarah Gallagher (Pennsylvania State University), and Jane Charlton (Pennsylvania State University), ref. 12.

Normally we would not expect to see such distant objects, so the standard big bang view of the universe assumes that 'quasars' are super-luminous black holes a million or a hundred million times more massive than our sun. Material from a surrounding disk causes the huge luminous emissions of energy as it falls into the black hole.

However, these assumptions are now being questioned, as a quasar has been reported[13,14] to be embedded in, and near to, the centre[15] of a *nearby* galaxy, NGC 7319 (see fig. 6.2). Certainly it is not behind the galaxy. In fig. 6.2, an arrow indicates the location of the high-redshift quasar. We see a V-shaped stream of gas trailing behind it, as would happen if it were ejected from the gas-filled region of the galaxy nucleus.

The quasar was initially found from its X-ray emission and subsequently identified in visible light with the Hubble Space Telescope. It has been classified as an ultra-luminous X-ray object (ULX), because of its very high emission of X-rays. Other ULXs have been found in, and near, galaxies, and astrophysicists Geoffrey and Margaret Burbidge and Halton Arp have suggested that they are quasars.[16]

From the Hubble Law and the galaxy redshift of $z = 0.022$, the galaxy should be at a distance of 360 million light-years. Again applying the Hubble Law to the quasar redshift, which is much larger at $z = 2.114$, we get a distance for the quasar of *billions* of light-years. So according to the prevailing big bang belief, these objects cannot be physically connected.

However, Arp has shown[17] that there is a very strong case that quasars are, in fact, physically associated with active galaxies to which they are adjacent. That is, the closeness is not just a trick of the line-of-sight, with the quasars millions or billions of light-years behind the galaxy. Arp (and others) have gone on to contend that the quasars have been ejected from the hearts of their adjacent parent galaxies,[18] and suggest that new galaxies are formed by this ejection mechanism.

The only way out is to claim that the alignment of the ULX quasar or QSO[19] in this report is merely an accident due to a line of sight effect. But the case against this is quite strong. It is seen interacting with gaseous material in the host galaxy. It seems that from the optical spectra of the QSO and the interstellar gas of the galaxy at $z = 0.022$ it is very likely that the QSO is interacting with the interstellar gas.[20]

In addition, a very strong outflow of gas is detected, consistent with the ejection of the quasar entraining material with it (see fig. 6.2). The authors of the report state

> … the QSO has been ejected from the nucleus of the Seyfert NGC 7319. It is seen that there is a luminous connection reaching from the nucleus … down in the direction of the ULX/quasar, stopping about 3" from it. It is also apparent that this connection or wake is bluer than the body of the galaxy ['Bluer' means that it is moving towards the observer relative to the galaxy (i.e. it was ejected)].

The idea that quasars are ejected from galaxies is vigorously rejected by the big bang community, as it demolishes their key assumption of the creation of all matter at the big bang. Furthermore, the evidence from quasars casts enormous doubt on the distribution of galaxies in the universe, and thus the interpretation of big bang expansion models.[7]

Appendix 5 gives details of preferred redshift values for the quasars and also evidence that only the low-

Figure 6.3: Interacting system that Arp claims shows galaxies being ejected from the central elliptical galaxy. It is believed to be mass transfer between the infrared luminous spiral (NGC 3561A) and the elliptical (NGC 3561B). Also seen are small dwarf galaxies at the tips of protrusions from the elliptical.

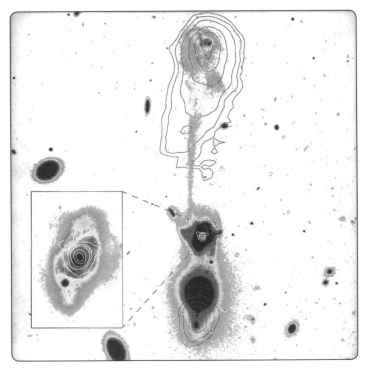

ESO/Duc P.A. *et al.*, ref. 22.

redshift quasars are similar to normal galaxies. The implication is that their large redshifts are intrinsic and are somehow related to the time of their creation. Because the quasar redshifts occur preferentially at certain values, and at other values there is a complete absence of quasars, this is further evidence for a galactocentric universe. This is because of the symmetry of these apparent concentric groupings of quasars. If each of these groupings were all created at the same time, it appears as if a series of creation episodes occurred as the cosmos was stretched out from a central point, all on Day 4.

Observations do, however, fit with the creationist cosmological model proposed in this book. The quasars are ejected from active galaxies in a grand creation process; and, as we observe the light from quasars today, we are effectively looking back in time (because it takes light a finite period of time to travel to Earth) to these creation events. This ejection process has been strongly promoted by Halton Arp as a secular interpretation of this evidence. See fig. 6.3, which may also be found in colour on the back cover of Arp's book *Seeing Red*.[21] It appears to show an elliptical galaxy ejecting smaller galaxies.

However, my interpretation is that we are seeing the creation process in the heavens as it was happening on Day 4 of Creation Week.[7] We are seeing creation as it happens! It certainly makes sense of what the psalmist said:

> 'The heavens declare the glory of God; the skies proclaim the work of his hands' (Ps 19:1).

These events make much more sense in light of a creation scenario where, according to the laws of physics which God created, as the universe expands, matter is created in a grand hierarchy and not all at some initial period shortly after some putative big bang. And this particle production process is a natural consequence[23] of the cosmological model I have outlined here.

Expansion factor

It is generally accepted that the universe has expanded over cosmic time. The question then remains: how much has it expanded since creation? Remember we are not considering that it began in a singularity as the big-bangers do.

A back-of-the-envelope calculation tells us that the universe expanded with an increase in volume of at least 36 billion times.[3] In comparison to the size of the universe at the present time it was very small. The calculation comes from the linear expansion factor $1 + z_{exp}$ where z_{exp} represents the redshift of the original light (electromagnetic radiation) that God created on Day 1. By assuming that this was visible light which would have had a radiant temperature of about 9,000 K and comparing this to the current temperature of the cosmic microwave background (CMB) radiation, which has a temperature of 2.7 K, we get an expansion factor of $1 + z_{exp} \approx 3,300$. This assumes that the CMB is somehow related to that original light source God created and that it has been adiabatically[24] cooled from 9,000 K to 2.7 K through the expansion of the cosmos. It also follows that the volume-expansion factor is $(1 + z_{exp})^3 = 3.6 \times 10^{10}$. This is the amount that space was stretched out.

Conversely, the density also decreased by 10 orders of magnitude if no new matter was created; but during the expansion process, new matter was continually created, so that would have tended to increase the density, slowing down the decrease, as time proceeded. At the present epoch, the average density of matter in the universe is about 10^{-31} g.cm^{-3}. So initially it could not have been more than about 10^{-21} g.cm^{-3}, which is about 10,000 hydrogen atoms in a cubic centimetre of space—that is still a very low density—a vacuum.

Based on my analysis of a galactocentric universe of finite size with a unique centre (see Appendix 4), I found that the physical radius of the universe must be at least the visible radius. The visible radius is determined from $c\tau$ and is approximately 13.5 billion light-years. Therefore it follows from the expansion factor that the initial radius of the universe was about 8 million light-years (possibly less) before God stretched out the heavens on Day 4 of Creation Week. This indicates that galaxies were initially created much closer to Earth, and then God expanded out the space, dragging them apart. And as that occurred, new material—additional galaxies, quasars etc.—was created like one of those fireworks displays where we see the exploding embers from the parent explosion in a chain reaction sequence.[25]

References

1. Charged Coupled Device—used in modern digital imaging.
2. Humphreys, D.R., *Starlight and Time,* Master Books, Colorado Springs, CO, 1994.
3. Hartnett, J.G., Cosmological expansion in a creationist cosmology, *J. of Creation* **19**(3):96–102, 2004.
4. Hartnett, J.G., The 'waters above', *J. of Creation* **20**(1):93–98, 2006.
5. Hartnett, J.G., Look-back time in our galactic neighbourhood leads to a new cosmogony, *J. of Creation* **17**(1):73–79, 2003.
6. Nur, A. and Walder, J., Time-dependent hydraulics of the earth's crust, Chapter 7 in *The Role of Fluids in Crustal Processes*, Geophysics Study Committee, National Research Council, National Academy Press, Washington, 1990.
7. Hartnett, J.G., The heavens declare a different story! *J. of Creation* **17**(2):94–97, 2003.
8. See<www.hubblesite.org/gallery/album/galaxy_collection/pr2006014a/>.
9. See <www.seds.org/messier/more/m087_h_nrao.html>.
10. See <www.vla.nrao.edu/>.
11. See <hubblesite.org/newscenter/archive/releases/2003/04/image/b>.
12. One galaxy from Stephan's quintet. See <www.hubblesite.org/gallery/album/entire_collection/pr2001022a/>.
13. See <ucsdnews.ucsd.edu/newsrel/science/mcquasar.asp>, University of California, San Diego web page, 10 January 2005.
14. Galianni, P., Burbidge, E.M., Arp, H., Junkkarinen, V., Burbidge, G. and Zibetti, S., The discovery of a high redshift X-ray emitting QSO very close to the nucleus of NGC 7319, *Ap. J.* **620**:88–94, 2005.
15. The quasar is measured to be 8 seconds of arc (8″) from the centre of the galaxy. There are 60 seconds in a minute of arc, 60 minutes in a degree and 360 degrees in a full circle. So 8″ is a very tiny angular measurement when looking out into space.
16. Burbidge, G., Burbidge, E.M. & Arp, H., The nature of the ultraluminous X-ray sources inside galaxies and their relation to local QSOs, *A & A*, **400**:L17–L19, 2003.

17. Arp, H., *Seeing red, redshifts, cosmology and academic science*, Apeiron, Montreal, 1998; Arp, H., *Quasars, redshifts and controversies*, Interstellar Media, Cambridge University Press, Berkeley, CA, 1987; Arp, H., Companion galaxies: a test of the assumption that velocities can be inferred from redshift, *Astrophysical Journal* **430**:74–82, 1994; Arp, H., The distribution of high-redshift ($z > 2$) quasars near active galaxies. *Astrophysical Journal* **525**:594–602, 1999; Arp, H., *Catalogue of Discordant Redshift Associations*, Aperion, Montreal, 2003.

18. Hartnett, J.G., Quantized quasar redshifts in a creationist cosmology, *J. of Creation* **18**(2):105–113, 2004.

19. QSO = Quasi-Stellar Object.

20. This is evident from the very strong oxygen-emission lines in the spectra of the gases of the galaxy adjacent to the quasar.

21. Arp, H., *Seeing Red: redshifts, cosmology and academic science*, Apeiron, Montreal, 1998.

22. Duc, P.A., Brinks, E., Wink, J.E. and Mirabel, I.F., Gas segregation in the interacting system Arp 105, *A & A* **326**:537–553, 1997.

23. Gemelli, G., Particle production in 5-dimensional cosmological relativity, *Int. J. Theor. Phys.* **45**(12):2261–2269, 2006; Gemeli, G., Hydrodynamics in 5-dimensional cosmological special relativity, *Int. J. Theor. Phys.* (in press) 2007, <arxiv.org/abs/gr-qc/0610010>.

24. No heat exchange in or out of the system. In a finite universe, this easily follows with no heat loss.

25. See DVD: Hartnett, J.G., *Hubble, Bubble, Big Bang in Trouble*, available from *Creation Ministries International*, <www.CreationOnTheWeb.org>.

Chapter 7:

Why we see starlight in a 'young' universe

Chapter 7: Why we see starlight in a 'young' universe

In the previous chapters, we learnt that, according to the creationary model presented here, our galaxy is somewhere near the unique centre of the universe created by God. We can observe His glory in the heavens all around us.

We also learnt that the universe is likely finite in size and has expanded (was stretched out) by an enormous factor since the initial creation. As a result of this expansion, new matter was created from the vacuum. This is a natural consequence of the conservation of mass/energy in the universe. (Note: while creating *ex nihilo*, God is not limited to His natural laws, which are, in any case, merely our descriptions of God's normal mode of upholding His creation in a regularly repeatable way. But, by assuming the principle of least assumptions, I conclude He uses His own laws where applicable.) What else naturally drops out of the new theory? Remarkably, the theory also provides an explanation for the light-travel-time problem.

The expansion of space caused an enormous time-dilation event on the earth, meaning that Earth clocks slowed by a trillion times compared to cosmic clocks. Time flowed in the cosmos at the same rate it does on Earth now, but during the time-dilation period, Earth's clocks ran slow. The actual factor can be estimated from the ratio of the Hubble–Carmeli time constant (τ)[1] to the length of time that time-dilation continued, as determined by Earth clocks. If the latter was over Day 4 only, then the time-dilation factor is at least a few trillion or more.[2]

During Creation Day 4 God created the heavenly bodies (stars and galaxies), and if Earth clocks ran slower by at least few trillion times (an outcome that 'falls out' of the new physics, as will be seen), then there would have been sufficient time (in a universe created some six thousand years ago by Earth clocks) for light to travel the vast distances of the universe. Light-travel-time problem solved! But let's look more closely at the mechanism; how it came about.

Which relativity theory?

Today we have the situation where Einstein's special relativity (SR) theory has been very successfully applied in the local laboratory frame with moving and stationary clocks, to GPS satellites, and in analyzing the decay of high-energy cosmic particles and also those from high-energy accelerators on Earth. Einstein's equivalence principle and his general relativity (GR) theory have also been extensively tested with space-borne clocks in rockets and satellites.

It appears that it also has been successfully applied to the large-scale structure of the cosmos—cosmology. The mathematical framework of Friedmann–Lemaître–Robertson–Walker (FLRW) is generally used nowadays to describe the expansion of the cosmos. However, various anomalies present themselves, including the mysterious 'dark' matter and 'dark' energy, which are said to comprise about

22% and 74% of the current universe, respectively. But these entities, though as yet undetected and unknown, are supposed to be all around us, filling the space we inhabit. There are notable research projects underway looking for the elusive WIMPS, axions[3] and other 'dark' matter particles like super-symmetric SUSY particles.[4] Yet none have been definitively discovered at the time of this writing.

Moreover, we are told that the universe underwent a rapid expansion—inflation[5]—this is the reason the CMB is so smooth and why we don't find magnetic monopoles.[6] There are also many other problems[7] with what has now become the standard paradigm—*the big bang* origin and evolution of the universe. It all seems to be unravelling at the seams.[8]

However, it might well be asked whether the application of GR (or *spacetime*) to the universe as a whole is correct. The underlying principle upon which the standard model is built is the Copernican or cosmological principle, as discussed previously. Another way of expressing the principle is that the physics that operates here and now is the same for the whole universe at all epochs of time. It also says that wherever the observer is, he will see essentially the same picture of the distribution of galaxies in the universe. But if that principle is wrong, then the model that results is invalid. And in chapters 5 and 6 and Appendix 5, the evidence shown suggests that that may well be the case.

Now the new Carmelian 4D *spacevelocity* cosmology questions the validity of applying GR to the large-scale structure of the universe. The success of its application to high-redshift supernova measurements, without the need for 'dark' matter and 'dark' energy fudge factors, certainly underlines the fact that there is an alternative explanation of the structure of the cosmos. The application of the same theory to the problem of the anomalous rotation curves in spiral galaxies required the 5D *spacetimevelocity* representation. But its success in reproducing the anomalously high speeds of the stars and gas in the disk regions, again without resorting to 'dark' matter, further strengthens the theory.

Let's now take special and general relativity as being correct on the local scale and also Carmeli's cosmological relativity as being correct on the galactic and cosmological scales. Then the only *spacetimevelocity* metric, which involves five dimensions, that can be correct on both the local scale, reproducing the 4D *spacetime* of special and general relativity (SR and GR) and on the cosmological scale, reproducing the 4D *spacevelocity* of cosmological relativity (CSR and CGR), is one that requires that enormous cosmological acceleration and accompanying time dilation has occurred, in the past, between Earth clocks and those in the rest of the universe. It logically follows that this means the universe is very young as measured by Earth clocks. It only has the appearance of great age because we are biased by the vast size of the universe.

This means that since the new theory is shown to fit the observations of the large-scale structure of the universe (see Appendix 2) and is consistent with Einstein's well-tested special and general relativity theories, then we are *forced to conclude* that the correct understanding of the expanding universe means that clocks on Earth once ran at much slower rates than clocks in the universe. I postulate that this was during Creation Week, specifically on Day 4. As a result, we have a mechanism for light to travel to Earth from the most distant galaxies within the biblical timescale.

Cosmological Relativity

Carmeli's 5D cosmological relativity contains all of Einstein's general relativity as a subset. All of the aspects of general relativity that have been experimentally established are also obtained in cosmological relativity.[9] On the local scale where the universe is not expanding, cosmological relativity has no application.

Cosmological special relativity (CSR) applies a framework, analogous to special relativity (SR), but to the whole cosmos without taking matter into account. When matter is added, cosmological general relativity (CGR) is required, analogous to general relativity.

CGR theory is considered using the same approach that Einstein applied, i.e. Riemannian geometry.[10] But in this case gravitation is described with a five-dimensional presentation in which the coordinates are those of Hubble (i.e. proper distances as measured by the Hubble Law and the measured redshifts of galaxies) and atomic time, as measured by Earth clocks.

The metric[11] used by Carmeli,[12] in a generally co-variant theory,[13] extends the number of dimensions of the universe by the addition of this new dimension —the radial velocity of the galaxies in the Hubble flow. The Hubble Law is assumed as a fundamental axiom for the universe and the galaxies are distributed accordingly. This is the critical point in understanding this thesis. The assumption is that during the creation of the heavenly bodies[14] on Day 4, the universe underwent a very rapid expansion. The new dimension describes the expansion of space which was rapidly stretched as the newly created galaxies were spread out throughout the expanding space.

The very fabric of space was stretched, and during that time of stretching, additional stars and galaxies were created.[15] In order to conserve energy (and because of the underlying conservation laws imposed by the Creator) the period also involved massive particle production. This conclusion naturally results from this 5D theory.[16] This involved the creation of the stars and galaxies via massive ejection events from the centres of active galaxies and quasars as discussed in the last chapter. Though still controversial, this idea has observational support. Halton Arp and other astrophysicists have published many papers and a few books[17] supporting this hypothesis based on decades of observations.

Their view is totally naturalistic, whereas in the creationary model presented here, all matter created this way was created during Day 4 by the Creator. This was part of the creation of the heavenly bodies, a process which we are still able to see from Earth

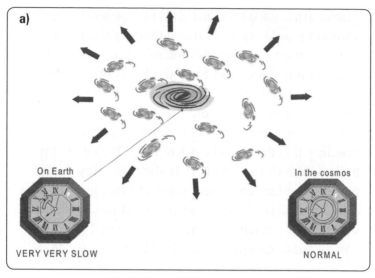

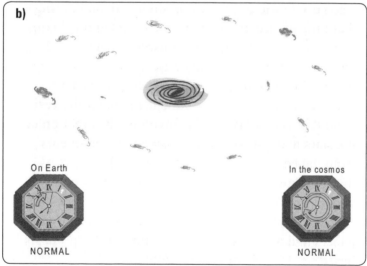

Figure 7.1 a) Illustration of galaxies rapidly moving out from our galaxy with Earth indicated. Two clocks are shown: Earth clock is running very slowly. Cosmic clock is running normally;

b) Illustration of galaxies very slowly moving out from our galaxy. Two clocks are shown: Earth and cosmic clocks are each running normally and therefore at the same rate.

with space-based and giant Earth-based telescopes, which reveal His Glory for all to see. Since, when we look out into the cosmos we are looking back in time, due to the finite speed of light, we are then looking at the events of Day 4 creation as they are actually happening. (This would also mean that the expansion of the universe only occurred during the creation period, over six thousand years ago as measured by Earth clocks.) The universe may no longer be expanding; at least the expansion is no longer accelerating. But we are seeing the after-effects of that expansion.

Therefore we expect that the environs of the solar system are not affected by any expansion now, which is consistent with the Hubble Law; i.e. no expansion locally. But outside the galaxy, residual effects are still observed, particularly towards the limit of observation. And it is at great distances and towards the limits of the visible universe where the CGR theory is most applicable. But since we are looking back in time, the very distant events actually occurred during the Creation Week. The same CGR theory requires that *the acceleration of the cosmos as measured by Earth clocks* be very large indeed. This is the same as saying that the timescale we make observations on in the cosmos is very short. I show in Appendix 2 that this same basis has been successfully applied to the high redshift (very distant) type Ia supernova observations.

This very rapid acceleration of the cosmos during Day 4 of Creation Week caused Earth clocks to run very slowly compared to cosmic clocks. (See fig 7.1(a).)

This, then, provides the massive time dilation needed to allow light to travel the vast distances of the universe, even billions of light-years *in a matter of days*—as measured by Earth Clocks. (See Appendix 6 for actual calculations.)

The question might be asked, 'Shouldn't we then see massive blueshifts because of the existence of the large time dilation between sources at the edge of the universe and those at the location of the observer?' No, the time dilation only occurred on Earth during the period of rapid expansion. Once the acceleration of the expansion stopped (i.e. once God stopped stretching out the fabric of space), there would be no difference in clock rates.[18] (See fig. 7.1(b).) And the acceleration was switched off six thousand years ago at the close of Day 4 on Earth. The omnipotent Creator caused the acceleration to be switched off throughout the universe when He stopped stretching out the fabric of space. If we were on Earth to observe the cosmos during the period when the acceleration stopped, we may have seen blueshifted starlight change colour as Earth clocks began to tick at approximately the same rate as cosmic clocks.

Conclusion

Within the framework of Carmelian cosmology, for the 5D theory to be consistent on all scales—that is, consistent with both special and general relativity on the local scale and cosmological general relativity on the largest scales—the acceleration of the fabric of the expanding universe must be extremely large at high redshift and zero in the solar system. This then leads to the conclusion that massive time dilation occurred at creation with respect to the observer at the centre of a spherically symmetric expanding universe. It also means that what we would calculate as the one-way speed of light (not the *actual* speed of light, which determines the physics in any local environment) would be extremely large at high redshift—a direct result of massive time dilation and not any change in the speed of light. Remember equation (2.1): time as the variable solves the conundrum. Therefore, light from the most distant galaxies could traverse the distances in a matter of a few days as measured by Earth-based atomic clocks, depending on the details of the magnitude of the past acceleration.

And there are no anomalous results on the aberration of starlight or any other well-proven relativistic effects, because the speed of light measured locally with atomic clocks is always the constant c. Light arriving at the earth is stretched by expansion (hence redshifts are observed), but because Earth-based clocks at the present epoch run at nearly the same rate as cosmic clocks, no other effects are observed.

The time-dilation effect occurred on Earth during the Creation Week as illustrated in fig. 7.1. When the acceleration of the expansion ceased, it caused the time dilation to cease, too. The universe may no longer be expanding; it's just that we see residual effects because of the finite travel-time of light.

An observer on Earth during the epoch of expansion would have seen large blueshifts. Currently, only redshifts are observed on the large scale in the universe. Everywhere within six thousand light-years of Earth the acceleration of the expansion can be observed to have ceased, and this sphere of observation expands as the light continues to arrive from farther and farther away. Therefore, events farther out are coming from Creation Week.

Observations are consistent with our galaxy being situated at the centre of a spherically symmetric universe of finite extent that has expanded many-fold. In terms of cosmological clocks, it is as if the universe appears like a still photograph. This is the result of the vast distances and slow intrinsic motions on the cosmological scale. Nevertheless, the validity of the new theory applying both to the current and past epochs leads to an inescapable conclusion: **the time it took light to travel from the most distant sources to Earth was a matter of only days, in local atomic time units.**[19]

References

1. The parameter $\tau \approx 4.28 \times 10^{17}$ s. Oliviera, F.J. and Hartnett, J.G., Carmeli's cosmology fits data for an accelerating and decelerating universe without dark matter or dark energy, *Found. Phys. Lett.* **19**(6):519–535, November 2006, <arxiv/abs/astro-ph/0603500>.

2. $\tau/(24 \text{ hours}) = 4.28 \times 10^{17}/86{,}400 \approx 5 \times 10^{12}$.

3. The axion is a hypothetical elementary particle postulated by Peccei–Quinn theory in 1977 to resolve the strong-CP problem in quantum chromodynamics (QCD). As of 2006, an experimental search by the PVLAS collaboration has reported results suggesting axion detection. This has not yet been confirmed by other searches. The name was introduced by Frank Wilczek, co-writer of the first paper to predict the axion. He named it after a brand of detergent—because the problem with QCD had been 'cleaned up'. For more details, see <www.wikipedia.org/wiki/Axion>.

4. See <www.en.wikipedia.org/wiki/Supersymmetry>.

5. In principle, the same idea of extremely rapid expansion of space is also suggested here, but the method (and underlying mechanism) and purpose is totally different. Also, the initial conditions are in no way similar.

6. See <www.en.wikipedia.org/wiki/Magnetic_monopole>.

7. Williams, A.R. and Hartnett, J.G., *Dismantling the Big Bang: God's Universe Rediscovered*, Master Books, Green Forest, AR, 2005.

8. Lerner, E.J. *et al.*, An open letter to the scientific community, *New Scientist* **182**(2448):20, 2004, <www.cosmologystatement.org>; Ratcliffe, H., The first crisis in cosmology conference, *Progress in Physics* **3**:19–24, 2005.

9. Carmeli, M., Accelerating Universe: Theory versus Experiment, <arxiv/abs/astro-ph/0205396>, 2002.

10. See <www.en.wikipedia.org/wiki/Riemannian_geometry>.

11. Actually a tensor; see <www.en.wikipedia.org/wiki/Metric_tensor>.

12. Behar, S. and Carmeli, M., Cosmological relativity: a new theory of cosmology, *Int. J. Theor. Phys.* **39**(5):1375–1396, 2000.

13. Generalizes the concepts of invariance; see <www.en.wikipedia.org/wiki/Covariant>.

14. The period of rapid expansion of the universe may have involved Days 1 through to 4, but the principle is the same.

15. Hartnett, J.G., The heavens declare a different story! *J. of Creation* **17**(2):94–97, 2003.
16. Gemelli, G., Particle production in 5-dimensional cosmological relativity, *Int. J. Theor. Phys.* **45**(12):2261–2269, 2006; Gemeli, G., Hydrodynamics in 5-dimensional cosmological special relativity, *Int. J. Theor. Phys.* (in press) 2007, <arxiv.org/abs/gr-qc/0610010>.
17. Arp, H., *Seeing Red: redshifts, cosmology and academic science*, Apeiron, Montreal, 2003; Arp, H., *Quasars, redshifts and controversies*, Interstellar Media, Cambridge University Press, Berkeley, CA, 1987.
18. Hartnett, J.G., A new cosmology: solution to the starlight travel time problem, *J. Creation* **17**(2):98–102, 2003.
19. In cosmic time, 'billions of years' is available for the light to travel. In effect, although c (the two-way measured speed of light) remains constant, the one-way speed of light to Earth has been dramatically increased by the expansion, enabling light to reach Earth within a short (Earth) time.

Technical Appendices

App. 1:   The large scale structure of the universe does not need 'dark' matter or 'dark' energy 122

App. 2:   The large scale structure of the universe tested against high redshift supernova measurements 135

App. 3:   Spiral galaxy rotation curves explained without 'dark' matter 157

App. 4:   A finite bounded universe with a unique centre 181

App. 5:   The Galaxy at the centre of concentric spherical shells of galaxies 199

App. 6:   Light-travel-time problem solved 219

Appendix 1: The large-scale structure of the universe does not need 'dark' matter or 'dark' energy

1. Motivation

The Carmeli cosmology is as revolutionary in its implementation as it is in its interpretation. Carmeli approached the problem of explaining the structure of the universe using new physics. No explicit cosmological constant or any 'dark' energy is employed, yet Carmeli initially assumed that the universe may contain some 'dark' matter. Ultimately, as these appendices will show, no 'dark' matter is necessary at all.

The new physics primarily involves a new dimension. Initially, Carmeli constructed his new theory as an analogue to special relativity in 4 dimensions. Then he developed it to a fully relativistic covariant theory in 5 dimensions. I would strongly recommend either of the books *Cosmological Special Relativity*[1] or *Cosmological Relativity*[2] for a comprehensive introduction to the theory.

Carmeli noticed that if one takes the flat *spacetime* interval of special relativity $ds^2 = c^2\, dt^2 - dr^2$ (written here in differential form, involving the Minkowski metric), where $dr^2 = (dx^1)^2 + (dx^2)^2 + (dx^3)^2$, (x^1, x^2, x^3) are spatial coordinates, c is the usual vacuum speed of light and t is the time coordinate, and then makes the substitutions $c \rightarrow \tau$ and $t \rightarrow v$, it becomes

$$ds^2 = \tau^2 dv^2 - dr^2, \qquad (A1.1)$$

where v is the speed of the expansion of the universe as measured by Hubble flow. Here the parameter τ is a universal time constant (called the Hubble–Carmeli constant) and its reciprocal, h, is approximately the Hubble constant H_0. Therefore, if one sets $ds = 0$, the equation (A1.1) becomes

$$dr^2 = \tau^2 dv^2 \approx H_0^{-2} dv^2, \qquad (A1.2)$$

which becomes the Hubble Law (in differential form) for an expanding universe when the positive square root is chosen.

2. 5D line element

Carmeli then carried this thinking over to the new metric, where he extended the number of dimensions of the universe by one, the radial velocity (v) of the galaxies in the expanding universe. Starting with the Minkowski line element $ds^2 = c^2 dt^2 - dr^2$, Carmeli added the velocity (v) of the expansion of space, which is scalar, because space expands uniformly in all directions. The new velocity dimension is *timelike*, resulting in a metric with signature $(+---+)$. Hence, the line element in five dimensions becomes

$$ds^2 = (1 + \frac{\Phi}{c^2})c^2 dt^2 - dr^2 + (1 + \frac{\Psi}{\tau^2})\tau^2 dv^2, \quad (A1.3)$$

where Φ and ψ are potential functions to be determined. The time t is measured in the observer's frame.

The line element (A1.3) represents a spherically symmetrical isotropic universe. The expansion is observed at a definite time and thus $dt = 0$. Taking into account $d\theta = d\phi = 0$ (the isotropy condition) and with the null condition $ds = 0$ (Carmeli's condition for Hubble expansion from section 1) then (A1.3) becomes

$$-dr^2 + (1 + \frac{\Psi}{\tau^2})\tau^2 dv^2 = 0. \quad (A1.4)$$

The solution of equation (A1.4) (given by equation (B.38) of ref. 1 and solved in section B.10) is reproduced here:

$$\frac{dr}{dv} = \tau\sqrt{1 + (1-\Omega)\frac{r^2}{c^2\tau^2}}. \quad (A1.5)$$

The parameter Ω is the mass/energy density of the universe expressed as a fraction of the critical or 'closure' density, i.e. $\Omega = \rho/\rho_c$, where ρ is the averaged matter/energy density of the universe. In this model, $\rho_c = 3/8\pi G\tau^2 \approx 10^{-29}$ g.cm^{-3}. Then (A1.5) may be integrated exactly to get

$$r = \frac{c\tau}{\sqrt{1-\Omega}}\sinh\left(\frac{v}{c}\sqrt{1-\Omega}\right) \forall \Omega . \qquad (A1.6)$$

3. Redshift versus distance

Carmeli expanded (A1.6) in the limit of small v/c and small Ω to get

$$r = \tau v\left(1+(1-\Omega)\frac{v^2}{6c^2}\right), \qquad (A1.7)$$

which clearly becomes the Hubble Law $r = \tau v$ for small velocities or redshifts. This is also the case where $\Omega = 1$ in (A1.7), which describes a coasting stage for the universe where it is neither accelerating nor decelerating—but provided the matter density $\Omega < 1$, equation (A1.7) represents an accelerating universe. Equation (A1.7) rewritten in natural units $(r/c\tau)$ as a function of redshift, $v/c = z$, is

$$\frac{r}{c\tau} = z\left(1+(1-\Omega)\frac{z^2}{6}\right). \qquad (A1.8)$$

Equation (A1.8) is plotted in fig. A1.1 for various values of $\Omega = 1$, 0.24 and 0.03. Curves above the $\Omega = 1$ line (broken line, the 'coasting' universe) represent accelerating universes where $\Omega < 1$, and curves below would represent decelerating universes where $\Omega > 1$. But the approximation used in (A1.8) requires that $|1-\Omega|z^2/6 \ll 1$. At low redshift, though, the curves cannot be resolved from each other. The theory must be tested at higher redshift where one can resolve the different models.

Equation (A1.6) written in terms of natural units for small z but arbitrary Ω is[3]

$$\frac{r}{c\tau} = \frac{\sinh\left(z\sqrt{1-\Omega}\right)}{\sqrt{1-\Omega}}. \qquad (A1.9)$$

Figure A1.1: Radial distance $r/c\tau$ versus redshift (z) from (A1.8) for $\Omega = 1$ (broken line), $\Omega = 0.245$ (solid black line) and $\Omega = 0.03$ (solid grey line).

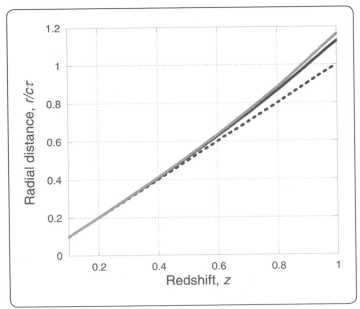

4. Matter density

Now let us consider what happens to the density of matter as we look back in the cosmos with redshift z. It was assumed in fig. A1.1 that the value of Ω is fixed for each curve. Carmeli also does this in fig. A4, page 134 in ref. 1. However, more correctly, Ω varies as a function of z. For flat space, matter density can be related to redshift by

$$\Omega = \Omega_m (1+z)^3, \qquad (A1.10)$$

where Ω is a function of the redshift z, and Ω_m is the averaged matter density of the universe at the current epoch. Note that when Carmeli solved (A1.5), he ignored the redshift dependence on Ω, saying that as the universe uniformly expands, at any epoch the density is the same across the universe. However, as observers, when we look back through space, hence through cosmic time, and therefore through redshift, we see the universe at different states of expansion. As a consequence (A1.10) results from this fact, which is the same as saying that as the redshift increases, the volume decreases as $(1 + z)^3$. Notice at $z = 1$ that the universe is 8 times smaller in volume and therefore 8 times more dense; that is, at $z = 1$, $\Omega = 8 \times \Omega_m$ ignoring any *spacevelocity* curvature.

Substituting (A1.10) into (A1.9), we get

$$\frac{r}{c\tau} = \frac{\sinh\left(z\sqrt{1-\Omega_m(1+z)^3}\right)}{\sqrt{1-\Omega_m(1+z)^3}}. \qquad (A1.11)$$

5. No 'dark' matter needed

Carmeli's equation was able to simulate the form of the $0.1 < z < 1$ redshift data from one of the high-redshift supernova teams[4] that published in 1998, announcing an accelerating universe. See fig. A4, page 134 in ref. 1. In fact, Carmeli had predicted[5] this in 1996 but he assumed a value of total matter (normal + 'dark' matter) density $\Omega = 0.245$, which was the accepted value in 1998 for Ω_m.

If we compare (A1.9) with $\Omega = 0.245$ and (A1.11) with $\Omega_m = 0.03$, we see from the first two rows of Table A1.1 (below) that $r/c\tau$ is essentially the same.

Redshift z	0.25	0.5	0.75	1.0
$r/c\tau$ from (A1.9) with $\Omega = 0.245$	0.25198	0.51598	0.80459	1.13157
$r/c\tau$ from (A1.11) with $\Omega_m = 0.03$	0.25246	0.51894	0.81042	1.13157
% diff. with $\Omega_m = 0.03$	0.19	0.57	0.72	0.00
% diff. with $\Omega_m = 0.04$	0.17	0.43	0.23	1.28

Table A1.1: Comparison of equations (A1.9) and (A1.11)

This means that my modified equation (A1.11) with $\Omega_m = 0.03$ gives the same result as Carmeli's unapproximated equation (A1.9) with his assumed value of $\Omega = 0.245$, except that Carmeli thought this included 'dark' matter. In fact, comparing (A1.9) and (A1.11), a local matter density of only $\Omega_m = 0.03 - 0.04$ is necessary to have agreement. This effectively means it *eliminates the need for the existence of 'dark' matter* on the cosmic scale. Certainly, the analysis can proceed without assuming any.

Table A1.1 shows the critical data from the comparison at redshifts between $z = 0.25$ and $z = 1$. It can be seen that the difference between the two equations over the domain of the measurements is negligible. If we assume $\Omega_m = 0.04$ instead of $\Omega_m = 0.03$, since both are within measured values of the local matter density,[6] we get closer agreement at smaller redshifts but worse near $z = 1$. As will be seen later, this is due to the density function not being accurate at higher redshift values.

In any case, (A1.9) and (A1.11) really must be modified as $z \to 1$ to allow for relativistic effects, by replacing $v/c = z$ with its relativistic form $v/c = ((1 + z)^2 - 1)/((1 + z)^2 + 1)$. This assertion is proven in Appendix 2, that the expansion of the universe is speed-limited, because it is discovered that only by using this form can a good fit to data be obtained without assuming a matter density greater than that observed locally. (See also ref. 7.) Therefore we can rewrite (A1.11) as

$$\frac{r}{c\tau} = \frac{1}{\sqrt{1-\Omega_m(1+z)^3}}\sinh\left(\frac{(1+z)^2-1}{(1+z)^2+1}\sqrt{1-\Omega_m(1+z)^3}\right),$$

$$(A1.12)$$

where the varying matter density has been taken into account. The density approximation (A1.10) may no longer be valid for $z > 1$.

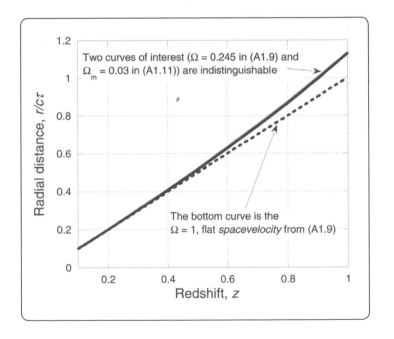

Figure A1.2: Plot of (A1.9) with $\Omega = 1$ (broken line) and $\Omega = 0.245$ (solid black line) and (A1.11) with $\Omega_m = 0.03$ (solid grey line). Note: the top two curves lay on top of each other.

6. Hubble parameter

Carmeli noted that H_0 has been measured with a scale dependence to its value. The greater the redshift, the smaller the determined value of Hubble's constant. Substituting $r = H_0^{-1} v$ from (4.1) into (A1.6) and using (A1.10) results in H_0, with a redshift dependence (compare to Carmeli's equation (A.54) in ref. 1) as

$$H_0 = h[1 - (1 - \Omega_m (1+z)^3) \frac{z^2}{6}], \quad (A1.13)$$

where it is also assumed that $|1-\Omega_m(1+z)^3|z^2/6 \ll 1$. Accordingly, (A1.13) (following equation (A.51) from ref. 1) may be further generalized without approximation, and using the relativistic form of the redshift it becomes

$$H_0 = h \frac{\xi}{\sinh\xi}, \quad (A1.14)$$

where $\quad \xi = \frac{(1+z)^2 - 1}{(1+z)^2 + 1} \sqrt{1 - \Omega_m (1+z)^3}$.

Equation (A1.14) is only approximate, however, for $z > 1$ because of the density assumptions.

Carmeli assumed a value of $H_0 \approx 70$ km.s^{-1} Mpc^{-1} at $z = 1$ in (A1.13), yielding a value $h \approx 80.2$ km.s^{-1} Mpc^{-1}, but if we use the relativistic form (A1.12) instead, we get $h \approx 73.27$ km.s^{-1} Mpc^{-1}. This means that without the small z approximation, the value of h is reduced when compared to that in ref. 1. In section 5 of Appendix 2, equation (A1.14) is the curve fitted to actual data.

7. No 'dark' energy

The cosmological constant (Λ) does not appear explicitly in Carmeli's theory. We'll see also, in Appendices 2 and 4, that 'dark' energy is not needed in the theory to make it fit observations. However, the effect of the expansion of the cosmos is encoded in the metric itself. In the FL theory, the 'dark' energy density Ω_Λ (i.e. the energy content of space due to the effect of a non-zero-value cosmological constant) is related to the cosmological constant by $\Omega_\Lambda = \Lambda/8\pi G$. In the CGR theory this is the energy of the vacuum, the stuff that space is made of. The physics of the cosmos is defined by the correct choice of the metric that is a solution of Einstein's field equations.

Now we observe the universe to be spatially flat—Euclidean. It has been one of the big questions of cosmology to answer, 'Why do we live at the present epoch where we observe the universe to be spatially flat?' I once received this as a question from one referee when I was trying to publish a paper of my analysis of the CGR theory and supernova data. The referee said that if I could answer this question he would accept my paper.

The present epoch matter density (i.e. Ω at $z \approx 0$) is most probably $0.02 < \Omega_m \leq 0.04$. To be flat or Euclidean the total mass/energy density of the universe ($\Omega_\Lambda + \Omega_m$) should be unity. In the *spacevelocity* theory, explained here, $1 - \Omega$ describes the curvature of *spacevelocity* and not of the 3D space in which we reside. We'll see in Appendix 4 that the correct understanding is that the total energy density of the universe is in fact the sum of the *spacevelocity* curvature and the matter content, which is always unity, hence space is Euclidean.

So what we observe is an expanding universe where the vacuum energy density $\Omega_\Lambda = 1$, always, and $\Omega_m \to 0$ as the universe expands—hence a spatially flat universe devoid of 'dark' matter. See Appendix 4 for more details.

References

1. Carmeli, M., *Cosmological Special Relativity*, 2nd ed. World Scientific, Singapore, 2002.
2. Carmeli, M., *Cosmological Relativity*, World Scientific, Singapore, 2006.
3. However one condition is imposed on the solution: $1 + (1 - \Omega)r^2 / c^2\tau^2 > 0$.
4. Riess, A.G., Filippenko, A.V., Challis, P., Clocchiatti, A. and Diercks, A., Observational evidence from supernovae for an accelerating universe and a cosmological constant, *Astron. J.* **116**(Sept):1009–1038, 1998.
5. Carmeli, M., Cosmological general relativity, *Communications in Theoretical Physics* **5**:159, 1996.
6. Fukugita, M., Hogan, C.J. and Peebles, P.J.E., The cosmic baryon budget, *Ap. J.* **503**:518–530, 1998.
7. Hartnett, J.G., The distance modulus determined from Carmeli's cosmology fits the accelerating universe data of the high-redshift type Ia supernovae without dark matter, *Found. Phys.* **36**(6):839–861, 2006, <arxiv.org/abs/astro-ph/0501526>.

Appendix 2: The large-scale structure of the universe tested against high-redshift supernova measurements

1. Introduction

In CGR, the usual Riemannian four-dimensional presentation of gravitation is used, except the coordinates are those of Hubble; i.e. distance and velocity, or more precisely, proper radial distances as measured by the Hubble Law and the measured redshifts of galaxies. The Hubble Law is assumed as a fundamental axiom for the universe and the galaxies are distributed accordingly. This results in a phase-space equation where the observables are redshift and distance. The latter may be determined from the high-redshift type Ia supernova (SNe Ia) observations.

In determining the large-scale structure of the universe, the usual time dimension is neglected as observations are taken over such a short time period compared to the motion of the galaxies in the expansion. In this case, $dt = 0$. This leaves only four dimensions to be considered—three of space and one of velocity.

Line element

Therefore, the 4D line element in CGR can be written as

$$ds^2 = \tau^2 dv^2 - e^\xi dr^2 - R^2(d\theta^2 + sin^2\theta\, d\phi^2)\,, \quad (A2.1)$$

where $dr^2 = (dx^1)^2 + (dx^2)^2 + (dx^3)^2$, ξ and R are functions of v and r alone and coordinates $x^\mu = (x^1, x^2, x^3, x^4) = (r, \theta, \phi, \tau v)$ are used. The new dimension (v) is the radial velocity of the galaxies in the expanding universe. It is not the time derivative of the distance. The parameter τ, the Hubble–Carmeli time constant, is a constant for all observers, and its reciprocal (designated h) is the Hubble 'constant', measured in the limit of zero gravity and zero redshift, which is only approximately the Hubble constant H_0.

Equation (A2.1), then, represents curved *space-velocity*, which, like in general relativity, may be represented by a four-dimensional Riemannian manifold with a metric $g_{\mu v}$ and a line element $ds^2 = g_{\mu v} dx^\mu dx^v$. This differs from general relativity in that here the x^4 coordinate is velocity-like, and similar to $x^0 = ct$. In this theory, $x^4 = \tau v$, where τ is a universal constant. The other three coordinates, x^k, $k = 1, 2, 3$, are space-like, as in general relativity. The line element represents a spherically symmetric, isotropic, but not necessarily homogeneous, universe.

Field equations

In CGR, as in general relativity, one equates geometry to physics. In this theory, Einstein's field equations

$$G_{\mu\nu} = R_{\mu\nu} - \frac{1}{2} g_{\mu\nu} R = \kappa T_{\mu\nu} \qquad \text{(A2.2)}$$

are modified. The energy–momentum tensor ($T_{\mu\nu}$) takes on a different physical meaning. The coupling constant (κ) that relates the geometry $G_{\mu\nu}$ in (A2.2) to the energy terms $T_{\mu\nu}$ is also different. However, the form of (A2.2) is exactly the same as in general relativity, but with $\kappa = 8\pi k/\tau^4$ and $k = G\tau^2/c^2$, where G is Newton's gravitational constant. As a result, $\kappa = 8\pi G/c^2\tau^2$.

The correspondence with general relativity is easily seen by the substitutions $c \rightarrow \tau$ and $t \rightarrow v$. In this new theory, the energy–momentum tensor $T^{\mu\nu}$ is constructed with these substitutions. As usual, $T^{\mu\nu} = \rho u^\mu u^\nu$, where ρ is the average mass/energy density of the universe and $u^\mu = dx^\mu/ds$ is a four-velocity.

In general relativity, $T_0^0 = c^2 \rho$. In Newtonian gravity, the potential function is defined by the Poisson equation $\nabla^2 \phi = 4\pi G\rho$. Where $\rho = 0$, the vacuum Einstein field equations are usually solved in general relativity, as is Laplace's equation ($\nabla^2 \phi = 0$) in the Newtonian theory. These are valid solutions, but in cosmology there never exists the situation where the mass/energy density (ρ) is zero, because the universe always contains matter and energy. So in order to equate the right-hand side of (A2.2) to zero, Carmeli took $T_4^4 \neq \tau^2 \rho$ but $T_4^4 = \tau^2 \rho_{eff} = \tau^2 (\rho - \rho_c)$. Here $\rho_c = 3/8\pi G\tau^2$ is the critical or 'closure' density. Therefore, in CGR, $T^{\mu\nu} = \rho_{eff} u^\mu u^\nu$.

The result is that we can view the universe, in *spacevelocity*, as being stress-free when the matter density of the universe is equal to the critical density. That is, the effective density $\rho_{eff} = 0$. This then gives us the analogous situation to that in the Newtonian and Einsteinian theories. Besides the assumption of the universality of the Hubble Law, this is the second fundamental assumption in this cosmology.

Phase-space equation

In CGR, the null condition $ds = 0$ describes the expansion of the universe. Therefore it follows from (A2.1) for a spherically symmetric distribution of matter

$$\tau^2 dv^2 - e^\xi dr^2 = 0, \qquad \text{(A2.3)}$$

which results in

$$\frac{dr}{dv} = \pm \tau e^{-\xi/2}. \qquad \text{(A2.4)}$$

The positive sign is chosen for an expanding universe. Equation (A2.4) has been solved in ref. 1. Because r, θ and ϕ are constants along the geodesics for the above chosen coordinates, $dx^4 = ds$ and therefore $u^\alpha = u_\alpha = (0,0,0,1)$.[2] Using this and equation (A2.2) rewritten as

$$R_{\mu\nu} = \kappa(T_{\mu\nu} - \frac{1}{2}g_{\mu\nu}T) , \qquad (A2.5)$$

where $T = T_{\mu\nu} g^{\mu\nu}$ and

$$T_{\mu\nu} = \rho_{eff}u_\mu u_\nu + p(u_\mu u_\nu - g_{\mu\nu}) , \qquad (A2.6)$$

where p is the pressure, one finds that the only non-vanishing components of $T_{\mu\nu}$ are $T_{44} = \tau^2 \rho_{eff}$, $T_{11} = pe^\xi \tau / c$, $T_{22} = pR^2 \tau / c$, $T_{33} = pR^2 \sin^2\theta \tau / c$ and $T = \tau^2 \rho_{eff} - 3p\tau / c$.

After some mathematical substitution, there remain only three independent field equations:

$$e^\xi(2R\ddot{R} + \dot{R}^2 + 1) - R'^2 = -\kappa e^\xi R^2 p\frac{\tau}{c} \quad (A2.7)$$

$$2\dot{R}' - R'\dot{\xi} = 0 \qquad (A2.8)$$

$$e^{-\xi}\left[\frac{R'}{R}\xi' - \left(\frac{R'}{R}\right)^2 - 2\frac{R''}{R}\right] + \frac{\dot{R}}{R}\dot{\xi} + \left(\frac{\dot{R}}{R}\right)^2 + \frac{1}{R^2} = \kappa\tau^2\rho_{eff} ,$$

$$(A2.9)$$

where the dots and primes denote differentiation with respect to v and r respectively.

2. Solution to field equations

Carmeli found a solution to the resulting field equations (A2.7)–(A2.9), with the necessary condition that $R' > 0$, as

$$R = r \qquad \text{(A2.10)}$$

and

$$e^{\xi} = \frac{1}{1 + f(r)} \ , \qquad \text{(A2.11)}$$

where $f(r)$ is an arbitrary function of r and satisfies $f(r) + 1 > 0$. The solution is where

$$f(r) = \frac{1 - \Omega}{c^2 \tau^2} r^2 \qquad \text{(A2.12)}$$

and $\Omega = \rho/\rho_c$. The matter density Ω is assumed to be the average density for matter that is evenly distributed throughout the universe. However, because we look back through past epochs, the density is a function of the redshift z.

By substituting (A2.11) and (A2.12) into (A2.4), we get Carmeli's result

$$\frac{dr}{dv} = \tau \sqrt{1 + (1 - \Omega) \frac{r^2}{c^2 \tau^2}} \ , \qquad \text{(A2.13)}$$

where the positive solution has been chosen for an expanding universe.

Equation (A2.13) may be integrated exactly to get

$$r = \frac{c\tau}{\sqrt{1-\Omega}} \sinh\left(\frac{v}{c}\sqrt{1-\Omega}\right) \forall \Omega . \quad \text{(A2.14)}$$

Written in terms of natural units $r/c\tau$ (A2.14) becomes

$$\frac{r}{c\tau} = \frac{\sinh(\beta\sqrt{1-\Omega})}{\sqrt{1-\Omega}} , \quad \text{(A2.15)}$$

where $v/c = \beta = ((1+z)^2 - 1)/((1+z)^2 + 1)$. Clearly β is a function of redshift z.

Considering the expansion of the universe, it follows that (A2.15) describes a tri-phase expansion. Initially, assuming the universe is very dense and $\Omega > 1$, the hyperbolic sine function becomes a normal trigonometric sine function, describing a decelerating expansion. Then the density Ω reaches unity and (A2.15) describes a coasting stage. Finally, the density decreases and becomes $\Omega < 1$ as the universe continues to expand. Then the hyperbolic sine function represents an exponentially accelerating universe.

There are three symbols used here for density expressed as a fraction of the critical density. The symbol Ω represents the matter density at any epoch defined by redshift z, and because we take $dt = 0$, Ω is therefore only a function of z. The symbol Ω_m represents the matter density at the present epoch and therefore is a constant on the timescale of any measurements used here. The symbol Ω_b specifically

represents the baryonic matter[3] density at the present
epoch, which, in this paper, we show to be identical
with Ω_m.

3. Matter density versus redshift

Carmeli assumed that the value of Ω in (A2.15) is
fixed, and plotted curves as functions of redshift
for various values of Ω as explained in Appendix 1.
More correctly, however, matter density is a function
of redshift z. And Carmeli never fitted his theory to
any of the high-redshift supernova data with a least-
squares method or any other, nor did he determine a
value for the matter density Ω_m.

The density of baryonic matter in the universe has
been estimated to be in the range $0.007 \leq \Omega_b \leq 0.041$
at $z \approx 0$, with a best guess of $\Omega_b \approx 0.021$, where a
Hubble constant of 70 km.s^{-1}Mpc^{-1} was assumed.[4] If
it can be shown that the present-epoch matter density
Ω_m needed to fit the observed data falls within that of
the baryonic budget, then no 'dark' matter need be
assumed.

Here I make no *a priori* assumptions about matter
density, dark, baryonic or otherwise, at high
redshift; however, I would proffer two models for
consideration. The first is the simple model, where
flat space is assumed,[5]

$$\Omega = \Omega_m (1+z)^3.$$ \hfill (A2.16)

Figure A2.1: Matter density as a function of redshift for both the approximated (broken-line) and exact transcendental (solid-line) models, with the same value of $\Omega_m = 0.04$. The transition redshift $z_t = 1.095$, where $\Omega = 1$ is indicated by the dashed lines.

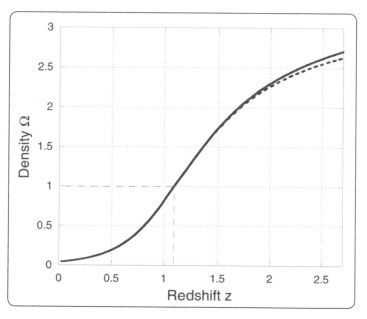

The second is based on a relativistic model, where the form for the mass of the universe is consistent with the solution for Einstein's equations for CGR and derived in section 2 of ref. 6. This matter density is shown as a function of redshift in fig. A2.1. To first order, it may be approximated by

$$\Omega \approx \Omega_m \frac{1 + \frac{1}{2}\beta^2}{(1-\beta)^3} . \qquad (A2.17)$$

In the limit of small β (i.e. for small z), equation (A2.17) becomes (A2.16).

The density function from (A2.17) is shown in fig. A2.1 with its unapproximated form—a transcendental function—yet, using Mathematica software, it can be plotted. Note that at redshift $z_t = 1.095$, where $\Omega = 1$ (indicated by the intersection of the dashed lines), the universe transitions from deceleration to acceleration.

In the Friedmann–Lemaitre–Robertson–Walker (FLRW) theory, the equivalent expression for (A2.16) is

$$\Omega = \Omega_m a^{-3}/H(a)^2, \qquad (A2.18)$$

where $a = (1+z)^{-1}$, the scale factor (because at the present epoch, as usual, a is assumed to be unity), and $H(a)$ is the Hubble term which quantifies the curvature of the expansion and is defined as $H^2 \equiv (\dot{a}/a)^2$, where the dot is the time derivative.

In the new theory, the curvature results from the inclusion of the new velocity dimension and the implicit assumption of the universality of the Hubble Law. This introduces curvature through the concept of *spacevelocity*. (The time derivative of a scale factor is not relevant.)

In the first instance, I assume the flat *spacevelocity* model of (A2.16), which is identical to (A2.18), where $H(a) = 1$. This would correspond to a dust-dominated, *spatially flat universe* in FLRW cosmologies for all redshift z, but this is not the case in the present theory (A2.17), where the density varies more strongly than $(1 + z)^3$. Since the unapproximated functional form for (A2.17) is transcendental, for fits to data, it is more convenient to have a regular function, and for the fit shown in this Appendix, a second order approximation is used. This is represented by the broken line in fig. A2.1.

4. Comparison with high-z type Ia supernova data

In order to compare (A2.15) with the data from the high-redshift SNe Ia teams, the proper distance is converted to magnitude (m) as follows:

$$m(z) = M + 5logD_L(z;\Omega), \qquad (A2.19)$$

where D_L is the dimensionless 'Hubble-constant-free' luminosity distance and

$$M = 5log\left(\frac{c\tau}{Mpc}\right) + 25 + M_B + a . \quad (A2.20)$$

The parameter M incorporates the various parameters that are independent of the redshift z. The units of $c\tau$ are Mpc.[7] The constant 25 results from the luminosity distance expressed in Mpc. The parameter M_B is the absolute magnitude of the supernova at the peak of its light-curve. However, M represents a scale offset for the distance modulus ($m-M_B$) or an arbitrary zero. It is sufficient to treat it as a single constant chosen from the fit. In practice, we use a, a small free parameter, to optimize the fits.

The luminosity distance (D_L) in CGR is related by

$$D_L(z;\Omega) = \frac{(1+z)}{\sqrt{1-\beta^2}} \frac{r}{c\tau} . \qquad (A2.21)$$

This is different from FLRW models by the factor $(1-\beta^2)^{-1/2}$. (See ref. 8 for a detailed derivation.)

The absolute magnitude M_B acts as a 'standard candle' from which the luminosity, and hence distance, can be estimated. Its value need not be known exactly. Neither does any other component in M, as M has the effect of merely shifting the fit curve (A2.21) along the vertical magnitude axis. (See fig. A2.2.)

However, by choosing the value of the Hubble–Carmeli constant, $\tau = 4.28 \times 10^{17}$ s $= 13.54$ Gyr, which is the reciprocal of the chosen value of the Hubble constant in the gravity-free limit $h = 72.17 \pm 0.84$ (statistical) km.s^{-1}Mpc^{-1} (see section 5) $M = 43.09 + M_B + a$.

Curve fits

For the analysis here, I have combined the data of two separate SNe Ia data sets. The data sets are drawn from table 5 of Riess et al.[9] of the High-z Supernova Search Team and tables 8 and 9 of Astier et al.[10] of the Supernova Legacy Survey.

Two fits are shown in fig. A2.2, the best statistical curve fit for the combined data set and the curve where $\Omega_m = 0.263$, which is the value that Astier et al.

conclude for the average matter density at the current epoch. The algorithm fits a least-squares method using the supplied data, without any weighting by the published errors. The best statistical fit resulted where $\Omega_m = 0.0401 \pm 0.0199$. This is the only free parameter besides a, which has no effect on the shape of the curve.

The best fit value of the matter density Ω_m is about twice the best guess value from the local ($z \approx 0$) cosmic baryon budget[4] but is still within the range estimate. The luminosity distance (D_L) function in (A2.21) is not sensitive to the value of Ω_m over the

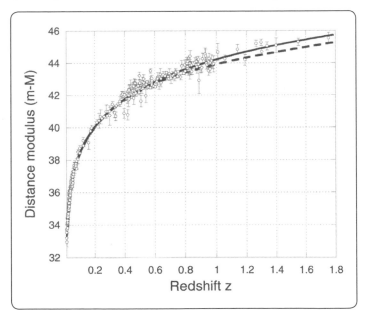

Figure A2.2: The combined data set of Riess *et al*. and Astier *et al*. The solid line represents the statistically best fit curve with a = 0.2284 and Ω_m = 0.0401, and the broken line represents the curve with a = 0.2284 and Ω_m = 0.263.

low-redshift range. Therefore, the value determined results from the high-redshift data. Also, it is possible, due to higher star formation at higher redshift that there is less neutral hydrogen than at low redshift. At low redshift, due to the lower occurrence of shock heating and hence ionization, less hydrogen is visible in the interstellar medium. This, though, is not 'dark' matter, as at most it means only twice the matter is needed over that which is observed at low redshift as baryonic matter. In the case of 'dark' matter, something like 10 times the baryonic matter is required when FLRW cosmologies are used.[11]

Moreover, Ω_m has been determined as a 'Hubble-constant-free' parameter because it comes from $D_L(z; \Omega_m)$, which is evaluated from fits using (A2.21). The latter is independent of the Hubble constant, or more precisely in this theory τ, the Hubble–Carmeli time constant. Therefore, Ω_m should be compared with Ω_b and not with $\Omega_b h^2$, where h is the Hubble constant as a fraction of 100 km.s^{-1}Mpc^{-1} (which is not to be confused with $h = 1/\tau$ used in CGR).

Nevertheless, the value of $\Omega_b h^2 = 0.024$ from the WMAP three-year results[12] and $h = 0.7217$ (assuming a value of $\tau^{-1} = 72.17$ km.s^{-1}Mpc^{-1}, see section 5) implies $\Omega_b = 0.043$, which is in good agreement with the results of this work. Yet caution must be advised as the resolution to the problem of the analysis of the WMAP data has not yet been attempted within the framework of CGR. Also, doubts have been raised as to the validity of the interpretation of the WMAP anisotropy map in light of the signal-to-noise ratio just above unity. And in light of the fact

Appendix 2: The large-scale structure of the universe tested against high-redshift supernova measurements

Figure A2.3: The residuals as a function of redshift (on linear scale): i.e. the differences between the best fit curve with $\Omega_m = 0.0401$ and a = 0.2284 and the data of fig. A2.2. The broken line represents the curve where $\Omega_m = 0.263$.

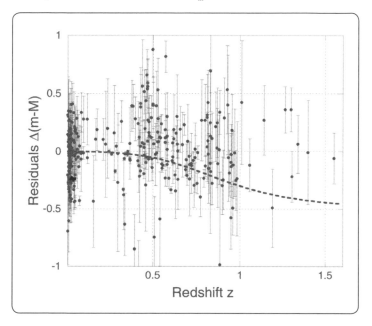

that the 'observed' anisotropies are extracted from a signal dominated by the one thousand times stronger Galactic foreground.[13]

Quality of fits

Looking at the two fits shown in fig. A2.2, it is clear that $\Omega_m = 0.263$ (broken curve) does not work in this model. The best fit (solid curve) has a statistical $\chi^2_{dof} = 0.074726$. This is the curve fit parameter χ^2 normalized by the number of data (N) less 1, which means per degree of freedom (dof). In this case

N = 302. The algorithm has been performed with 1 σ errors equal to unity.[14] From the most probable value $\Omega_m = 0.0401 \pm 0.0199$, since this is within the baryonic matter density range, no exotic 'dark' matter need be assumed.

Fig. A2.3 shows the residuals between the data and this best statistical fit (solid curve of fig. A2.2) for the combined data set. The mean of the residuals is 8.04×10^{-5} when all errors are assumed equal (and unity) and -0.0769 when weighted by published errors.

The χ^2_{dof} is extremely good, even compared to the N = 185 data set of Riess et al. alone, which was fitted in fig. 1 of ref. 5 with (A2.15), but without the additional factor $(1 - \beta^2)^{-1/2}$ in the luminosity distance (A2.21). That resulted in $\chi^2_{dof} = 0.2036$. Using the larger data set, and the improved model, χ^2_{dof} is about three times smaller.

The improvement, though, has largely resulted from the additional factor $(1 - \beta^2)^{-1/2}$ in the luminosity distance (A2.21) and only a little from the refinement of the density model. If we exclude the new density model (A2.17) and use instead the simpler model (A2.16) with $\Omega_m = 0.04$, we get $\chi^2_{dof} = 0.075986$ for the best fit to the combined data set (requiring $a = 0.2152$).

5. Values of some key universal parameters

Hubble constant

Using the small redshift limit of (A2.15) and the Hubble Law at small redshift ($v = H_0 r$), it has been shown in (A1.13) that the Hubble parameter H_0 varies with redshift. If (A1.13) applies at the low redshift limit, it follows from the theory that at high redshift we can write

$$H_0 = h \frac{\beta \sqrt{1-\Omega}}{\sinh(\beta \sqrt{1-\Omega})} . \qquad (A2.22)$$

Therefore, H_0 in this model is redshift-dependent, not constant, and $H_0 \leq h$. Only $h = \tau^{-1}$ is truly independent of redshift and constant. The condition where $H_0 = h$ only occurs at $z = 0$ and where $\Omega \to 0$.

By plotting H_0 values determined as a function of redshift, using (A2.22), it is possible to get an independent determination of h, albeit the noise in the data is very large. This is shown in fig. A2.4 with values calculated by two methods, with the exception of one point at $z = 0.333$. See figure caption for details. The data, even though very scattered, do indicate a downward trending of H_0 with redshift.

Separate curve fits from (A2.22), with h as a free parameter, have been applied to two data sets, Tully–Fisher (TF) (the solid line) and SNe Ia (the broken line) measurements. The former resulted in $h = 72.47 \pm 1.95$ (statistical) ± 13.24 (rms) $km.s^{-1}Mpc^{-1}$ and from the latter $h = 72.17 \pm 0.84$ (statistical) ± 1.64 (rms) $km.s^{-1}Mpc^{-1}$. The rms errors are those derived from the published errors; the statistical errors are those due to the fit to the data alone. The SNe Ia determined value is more tightly constrained but falls within the TF determined value.

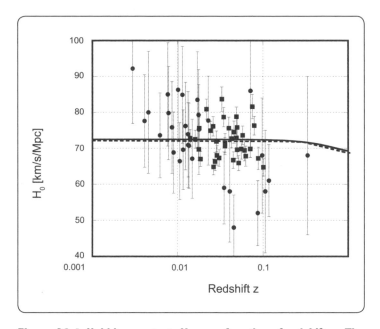

Figure A2.4: Hubble constant, H_0, as a function of redshift z. The filled circles are determined from Tully–Fisher measurements taken from ref. 15, table 5 of ref. 16 and table 7 of ref. 17, except that the point at $z = 0.333$ is from the Sunyaev–Zel'dovich effect taken from fig. 4 of ref. 16. The filled squares are determined from the SNe Ia measurements and taken from table 6 of ref. 17 and table 5 of ref. 18. The errors are those quoted in the sources from which the data was taken.

If we choose $h = 72.17$ km.s^{-1}Mpc^{-1} from SNe Ia measurements and take it reciprocal, we get a value for $\tau = 13.54 \pm 0.48$ Gyr.

Mass of the universe

It can be shown[6] that

$$\Omega_m = \frac{R_S}{R_0} , \qquad (A2.23)$$

where $R_s = 2GM_0/c^2$ is the Schwarzschild radius if the present universe rest mass M_0 is imagined to be concentrated at a point, and $R_0 = c\tau$ is the present radius of the visible universe. From this we get the present universe rest mass:

$$M_0 = \Omega_m \frac{c^3 \tau}{2G} , \qquad (A2.24)$$

which, with $\Omega_m = 0.0401 \pm 0.0199$ gives $M_0 = (1.74 \pm 0.86) \times 10^{21} M_\odot$.[19] And the average matter density is $(3.92 \pm 1.94) \times 10^{-31}$ g.cm^{-3}.

6. Conclusion

The analysis here has shown that the most probable value of the present epoch density of the universe is $\Omega_m = 0.04$, with a statistical 1σ error of 0.02 determined from the best fit to a data set of 302 high-redshift distance–magnitude data. The fits used a density function with limited range and validity and did not take into account the published errors on the individual magnitude data. The fits to the data are consistent over the entire range of the available redshift data, from $0.1 < z < 2.0$, a result of the more accurate relation for Ω, as well as the proper accounting of the increase in the source luminosity due to the factor $(1 - \beta^2)^{-1/2}$.

Since Ω_m is within the baryonic matter-density budget, there is no need for any 'dark' matter to account for the SNe Ia redshift magnitude data. Furthermore, since the predicted transition redshift[20] $z_t = 1.095^{+0.264}_{-0.155}$ is well within the redshift range of the data, the expansion rate evolution from deceleration to acceleration, which occurred about 8.54 Gyr ago, by cosmological clocks, is explained without the need for any 'dark' energy. No cosmological constant (Λ) appears in Einstein's field equations in the Carmeli theory. The 'force' pushing the universe apart, which invokes 'dark' energy in many an astrophysicist's mind, is more correctly just a property of the correct metric. Finally, it has been shown that the theory is consistent with the high-redshift data presented here without invoking any 'dark' matter at all.

References

1. Carmeli, M., *Cosmological Special Relativity*, 2nd ed. World Scientific, Singapore, 2002.
2. In Appendix A.3 of ref. 1, the zeroth coordinate is velocity in Carmeli's 4D representation, but for consistency with the 5D metric used later, I define it as the fourth coordinate here.
3. Baryons are normal matter particles such as protons and neutrons.
4. Fukugita, M., Hogan, C.J. and Peebles, P.J.E., The cosmic baryon budget, *Ap. J.* **503**:518–530, 1998.
5. Hartnett, J.G., The distance modulus determined from Carmeli's cosmology fits the accelerating universe data of the high-redshift type Ia supernovae without dark matter, *Found. Phys.* **36**(6):839–861, 2006. <arxiv.org/abs/astro-ph/0501526>.
6. Oliveira, F.J. and Hartnett, J.G., Carmeli's cosmology fits data for an accelerating and decelerating universe without dark matter or dark energy, *Found. Phys. Lett.* **19**(6):519–535, 2006. <arxiv.org/abs/astro-ph/0603500>.
7. Mpc = megaparsecs = 3.0856×10^{22} m.
8. Hartnett, J.G. and Oliveira, F.J., Luminosity distance, angular size and surface brightness in Cosmological General Relativity, *Found. Phys.* **37**(3):446–454, 2007. <arxiv.org/abs/astro-ph/0603500>.
9. Riess, A.G. *et al.*, Type Ia supernovae discoveries at $z > 1$ from the Hubble Space Telescope: Evidence for past deceleration and constraints on dark energy evolution, *Ap. J.* **607**:665–687, 2004.
10. Astier, P. *et al.*, The Supernova Legacy Survey: Measurement of Ω_m, Ω_Λ and w from the first year data set, *A&A* **447**:31–48, 2006.
11. Compare 0.22 'dark matter' (= 0.263 matter − 0.04 baryonic) at high redshift to 0.02 best guess baryonic matter at low redshift.
12. Spergel, D.N. *et al.*, Wilkinson Microwave Anisotropy Probe (WMAP) three year results: Implications for cosmology, <arxiv.org/abs/astro-ph/0603449>.
13. Robitaille, P-M., WMAP: A radiological analysis, *Progress in Physics*, **1**:3–18, January 2007.
14. See discussion section 5 in ref. 8.
15. Freedman, W.L. *et al.*, Distance to the Virgo cluster galaxy M100 from Hubble Space Telescope observations of Cepheids, *Nature* **371**:757–762, 1994.

16. Tutui, Y. *et al.*, Hubble constant at intermediate redshift using the CO-Line Tully-Fisher relation, *PASJ.* **53**:701, <arxiv.org/abs/astro-ph/0108462>, 2001.
17. Freedman, W.L. *et al.*, Final results from the Hubble Space Telescope Key Project to measure the Hubble constant, *Ap. J.* **553**:47–72, 2001.
18. Riess, A.G. *et al.*, Type Ia supernovae discoveries at $z > 1$ from the Hubble Space Telescope: Evidence for past deceleration and constraints on dark energy evolution, *Ap. J.* **607**:665–687, 2004.
19. $M_{\odot} = 1$ solar mass unit $= 2 \times 10^{30}$ kg.
20. Uncertainties were determined in ref. 6.

Appendix 3: Spiral galaxy rotation curves explained without 'dark' matter

1. Introduction

The rotation curves highlighted by the circular motion of stars, or more accurately characterized by the spectroscopic detection of the motion of neutral hydrogen and other gases in the disk regions of spiral galaxies, have caused concern for astronomers for many decades. Newton's Law of Gravitation predicts much lower orbital speeds than those measured in the disk regions of spiral galaxies.

The most luminous galaxies show slightly declining rotation curves (orbital speed versus radial position from nucleus) in the regions outside the star-bearing disk, coming down from a broad maximum in the disk. Intermediate mass galaxies have mostly nearly flat rotation speeds along the disk radius. Lower luminosity galaxies usually have monotonically increasing orbital velocities across the disk.

The traditional solution has been to invoke halo 'dark' matter that purportedly surrounds the galaxy but is transparent to all forms of electromagnetic radiation. In fact, astronomers have traditionally resorted to 'dark' matter whenever known laws of physics were unable to explain the observed dynamics.

In 1983, Milgrom introduced his MOND,[1] an empirical approach, which attempts to modify Newtonian dynamics in the region of very low acceleration. Newton's Law describes a force proportional to r^{-2}, where r is the radial position from the centre of the matter distribution, but Milgrom finds that an r^{-1} law fits the data very well.[2]

Carmeli approached the problem from a different perspective. He formulated a modification, actually an extension of Einstein's general theory, in an expanding universe, taking into account the Hubble expansion as a fundamental axiom, which imposes an additional constraint on the dynamics of particles.

Carmeli believes the usual assumptions in deriving Newton's Gravitational Force Law from general relativity are insufficient, that gases and stars in the 'arms' of spiral galaxies are not immune from Hubble flow. As a consequence, a universal constant a_0 (in this case, slightly different to Milgrom's) is introduced as a characteristic acceleration in the cosmos. Using this theory, Carmeli successfully provided a theoretical description of the Tully–Fisher Law.[3] Following Carmeli's lead, I was able to extend the analysis[4] to the gravitational potential and the resulting forces that determine how test particles move in the disks of spiral galaxies using cylindrical coordinates and an exponential matter-density distribution.

Two acceleration regimes were discovered. In one, normal Newtonian gravitation applies. In that regime, the effect of the Hubble expansion is not observed or is extremely weak. It is as if the particle accelerations are so great that they slip across the expanding space. In the other, new physics is needed. There, the Carmelian metric provides it. In this regime, the accelerations of particles are so weak that their motions are dominated by the Hubble expansion, and as a result particles move under the combined effect of both the Newtonian force and a post-Newtonian contribution.

2. Gravitational potential

In the weak gravitational limit, where Newtonian gravitation applies, it is sufficient to assume the Carmeli metric with non-zero elements
$g_{00} = 1 + 2\phi/c^2$, $g_{44} = 1 + 2\psi/\tau^2$, $g_{kk} = -1$ $(k = 1, 2, 3)$
to the lowest approximations in both $1/c$ and $1/\tau$. The potential functions ϕ and ψ are determined from Einstein's field equations and from their respective Poisson equations,

$$\nabla^2\phi = 4\pi G\rho, \qquad \text{(A3.1a)}$$

$$\nabla^2\psi = \frac{4\pi G\rho}{a_0^2}, \qquad \text{(A3.1b)}$$

where ρ is the matter density and a_0 a universal characteristic acceleration $a_0 = c/\tau$.

In cylindrical coordinates (r, θ, z), the potential ϕ that satisfies (A3.1a) has been found,[5]

$$\phi(r) = -2\pi G \int_0^\infty J_0(kr)dk \int_0^\infty \rho(r')J_0(kr')r'dr', \quad (A3.2)$$

where $J_0(kr)$ is the zeroth order Bessel function and k is the z-coordinate scale factor ($k = 1/b$).

It is also assumed that the density function can be modelled as a delta function of the vertical coordinate z. Therefore we can write the density $\rho(r,z) = \rho(r)\rho(z) = \rho(r)\delta(z)$ with no azimuthal θ-dependence. To correctly model the effect of the spiral arms, some θ-dependence may be needed, but for our model it is assumed independent. The requirement on the z-dependence is satisfied with density functions of the form

$$\rho(z) = \frac{1}{2b} sech\left(\frac{z}{b}\right)^2 \quad or \quad e^{-|z|/b}. \quad (A3.3)$$

Provided the scale length b is much smaller than the limit of the actual matter distribution in the z-direction, then the integral over all z yields a contribution to the mass of unity. This is the thin disk approximation, which seems to be fairly applicable over both disk and galactic bulge.

The integral over dk in (A3.2) is the surface density, which may be calculated once the form of the density ρ is known. From observations of spiral galaxies, it is clear that the density function needs an exponential dependence in the radial direction. An appropriate function is of the form

$$\rho(r) = \frac{M}{2\pi a^2} e^{-r/a}, \tag{A3.4}$$

where a is a radial scale length and M is the mass of the galaxy.

3. Equations of motion

The Hubble Law describes the expansion of the cosmos and the matter embedded in it. Therefore, the 5D line element in *spacetimevelocity* is

$$ds^2 = g_{00}c^2 dt^2 + g_{kk}(dx^k)^2 + g_{44}\tau^2 dv^2, \tag{A3.5}$$

where $k = 1, 2, 3$. The relative separation in 3 spatial coordinates $r^2 = (x^1)^2 + (x^2)^2 + (x^3)^2$ and the relative velocity between points connected by ds is v, for particles subject to the Hubble expansion.

Carmeli solved Einstein's field equations in five dimensions to find the relevant equations of motion. It resulted in the following equations, reproduced from (B.62a) and (B.63a) of ref. 6 to lowest approximation in $1/c$,

$$\frac{d^2 x^k}{dt^2} = -\frac{1}{2}\frac{\partial \phi}{\partial x^k}, \tag{A3.6}$$

This is the usual-looking geodesic equation derived from general relativity but now in five dimensions. And the second is a new 'phase space' equation derived from the Carmeli theory,

$$\frac{d^2 x^k}{dv^2} = -\frac{1}{2}\frac{\partial \psi}{\partial x^k} \, . \tag{A3.7}$$

Newtonian

It follows from (A3.6), (A3.4) and (A3.2), and the usual circular motion equation

$$\frac{v^2}{r} = \frac{d\phi}{dr}, \tag{A3.8}$$

that

$$v^2 = \frac{GMr^2}{2a^3}\Pi \, , \tag{A3.9}$$

where G denotes the gravitational constant and

$$\Pi = I_0\!\left(\frac{r}{2a}\right)\!K_0\!\left(\frac{r}{2a}\right) - I_1\!\left(\frac{r}{2a}\right)\!K_1\!\left(\frac{r}{2a}\right), \tag{A3.10}$$

where I and K are standard zeroth and first order Bessel functions.

Equation (A3.9) is the usual Newtonian result for the speed of circular motion in a cylindrical gravitational potential. This equation has been plotted in curve 3 of figs. A3.2(a)–A3.6(a) as a function of radial position from the centre of a galaxy in kiloparsecs (kpc), where kpc $\approx 3.09 \times 10^{19}$ m. Best fits were determined with M and a as free parameters. The mass M is expressed in solar mass units $M_{\odot}$.[7]

Carmelian

Using $\psi = \phi / a_0^2$ in (A3.7) results in a new equation

$$v = a_0 \int_0^r \frac{dr}{\sqrt{-\phi}}, \qquad (A3.11)$$

which is integrated and solved for v as a function of r. Using the potential ϕ, determined from (A3.2) and (A3.4), in (A3.11), results in

$$v = \frac{2}{3} a_0 \frac{r^{3/2}}{\sqrt{GM}}, \qquad (A3.12)$$

which describes the expansion of space within a galaxy.

Even though v is scalar, it must be realized that in the cylindrical coordinates of a galaxy the only direction that is free to expand in the Hubble flow is the azimuthal.[8] Therefore (A3.12) describes the velocity component in that direction. Carmeli applied this line of reasoning.[3]

To establish the combined result of the two equations of motion, (A3.9) and (A3.12), the simultaneous speed of test particles must be determined by the elimination of r between the two equations. The physical meaning can be understood in terms of particles that simultaneously satisfy both (A3.6) and (A3.7).

The usual Newtonian expression (A3.6) describes motion under the central potential but assumes that spatial coordinates are fixed, whereas the new equation, (A3.7), describes the expansion of space itself within a galaxy. Therefore we must find

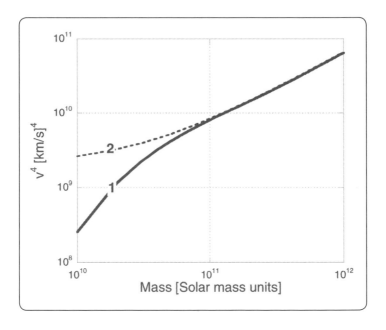

Figure A3.1: Tully–Fisher Law plotted on logarithmic axes. Curve 1 (solid line) represents the fourth order dependence of the rotational speeds of tracer gases in galaxies determined from the Carmelian equation (A3.13). The masses are expressed in solar mass units of 2 × 10³⁰ kg. Curve 2 (broken line) represents the straight line $v^4 = 2\times10^9 + 0.064M$.

the combined (simultaneous) effect of (A3.9) and
(A3.12). The result is a post-Newtonian equation,

$$v^{2/3} = \frac{(GM)^{5/3}}{\left(\frac{2}{3}a_0\right)^{4/3} 2a^3} \Pi, \qquad \text{(A3.13)}$$

derived from (A3.9), where the following substitution

$$r \to \left(\frac{GMv^2}{\left(\frac{2}{3}a_0\right)^2}\right)^{1/3}$$

has been made from (A3.12). The resulting equation,
hereafter referred to as Carmelian, cannot be solved
analytically. However, using the Mathematica
software package, (A3.13) can be solved numerically.

The result is plotted in curve 1 of fig. A3.1, where it
has been assumed that $a = 1$ kpc and it is compared
with the straight line $v^4 = 2 \times 10^9 + 0.064M$ (curve 2).
For large M, the small offset can be neglected. This
result indicates that the fourth order dependence on
rotational speed (v) is directly proportional to mass
(M) for large masses.

Assuming that the masses of the galaxies studied
are directly proportional to their luminosity,
this dependence then becomes the Tully–Fisher
relationship. This extends the work of Carmeli and
derives the underlying theoretical framework upon
which the Tully–Fisher Law is founded.

4. Rotation curves

In refs 3 and 8, using spherical coordinates, it was found that in the limit of large r and where all the matter was interior to the position of a test particle, such a particle is also subject to an additional circular motion described by (A3.12). Apparently, this is the result of the expansion of space itself within the galaxy but is in an azimuthal direction to the usual centre of coordinates of the galaxy. Here the same result (A3.12) is obtained, but in this case derived using cylindrical coordinates.

Carmeli[9] determined a Tully–Fisher-type relation using the Newtonian circular velocity equation expressed in spherical coordinates,

$$v^2 = \frac{GM}{r},$$ (A3.14)

where it is assumed that test particles orbit at radius r outside of a fixed mass M. Then by eliminating r between (A3.14) and (A3.12) we get the result. This is achieved by raising (A3.14) to the $\frac{3}{2}$ power and multiplying it by (A3.12), yielding

$$v^4 = GM\frac{2}{3}a_0.$$ (A3.15)

So, by applying the same approach with (A3.9), raising it to the $\frac{3}{2}$ power and multiplying it by

(A3.12), we can derive an equation describing the rotation curves in galaxies. The result is

$$v^4 = GM \frac{2}{3} a_0 \left\{ \left(\frac{r}{2a} \right)^{9/2} 8\, \Pi^{3/2} \right\}, \qquad \text{(A3.16)}$$

remembering that Π is a function of $r/2a$. It is easily confirmed that as $r \to \infty$,

$$\left(\frac{r}{2a} \right)^{9/2} 8\, \Pi^{3/2} \to 1 \, ,$$

which is the only part of equation (A3.16) that is dependent on the radial position (r). Hence, (A3.16) recovers the form of the Tully–Fisher relation (A3.15).

By taking the fourth root of (A3.16), we get an expression for the circular velocity of test particles as a function of their radial position r. That result has been plotted in curve 2 of figs. A3.2(a)–A3.6(a) for each galaxy, with a and M determined as fit parameters. The resulting curves have the characteristic flat shape for large radial position r. At small values of r, the rotation speeds determined from the Newtonian equation (curve 3) dominate, as seen in figs. A3.3(a)–A3.6(a).

5. Accelerations

The acceleration $\frac{2}{3} a_0$ in (A3.12) can be considered to be a critical acceleration. Therefore, when we compare the accelerations derived from the Newtonian equation (A3.9) and the Carmelian equation (A3.16) with this critical acceleration, we notice two regimes develop. See figs. A3.2(b)–A3.6(b).

For example, fig. A3.3(b) is very instructive. There, the straight line (curve 1) is the critical acceleration $\frac{2}{3}a_0$, curve 2 represents the acceleration derived from the Carmelian equation (A3.16) and curve 3 represents the acceleration derived from the Newtonian equation (A3.9). For the values, determined from the fits, of the mass (M) and the radial scale length (a), which determine how the matter density varies as a function of radial position r, curves 2 and 3 cross each other very close to the critical acceleration. The significance is that for accelerations less than the critical acceleration, the Carmelian force applies, and for those greater than the critical acceleration, the Newtonian force applies. Note also that the Newtonian curve 3 has an r^{-2} dependence and the Carmelian curve 2 has an r^{-1} dependence above 10 kpc. When curves of the form r^{-x} were fitted to the functions used in fig. A3.3(b), between 15 and 20 kpc, the coefficients x were determined to be $x = 2.003$ and $x = 1.025$ respectively.

From (A3.9), the gravitational acceleration (v^2/r) can be calculated in the limit of $r \to \infty$, outside most of the matter of the galaxy. As expected for the Newtonian model, it tends to GM/r^2. And similarly, from (A3.16) the gravitational acceleration (v^2/r) can be calculated in the limit of large r, for the Carmelian model. In this case, it is evident from (A3.15) that it must tend to $\frac{1}{r}\sqrt{GM\frac{2}{3}a_0}$. In this regime, the accelerations are very weak. This is very significant, as alternative theories of gravity have been suggested (for example, Milgrom, ref. 2), where the force of gravity falls away as r^{-1} for small accelerations. However, for small r, close to the origin of the central gravitational potential, the effect of the Carmelian force law becomes extremely small and is many orders of magnitude smaller than that for the Newtonian force law.

6. Sample of galaxy rotation curves

A sample of 5 galaxy fits are shown in figs. A3.2–A3.6. The top (a) figures show the rotation curve fits and the bottom (b) figures show the resulting acceleration regimes. In each figure, the measured rotational speeds of tracer gases in the chosen spiral galaxy are shown as a function of radial position (curve 1). Measured data are taken from ref. 10 for figs. A3.2–A3.5.

Theoretical curves from the Carmelian equation (A3.19) (curve 2) and from the Newtonian equation (A3.9) (curve 3) are fitted over the range of r that best fits the data by allowing a and M to be free parameters. The best fit values of these are shown in table A3.1. They are compared with some published values of a and masses determined from different methods.

The accelerations in the bottom (b) figures are derived from the Carmelian (curve 2) and the Newtonian (curve 3) equations respectively, with values of a and M derived from the fits in the (a) figures. These are compared with (curve 1), the critical acceleration $\frac{2}{3}a_0 \approx 4.7 \times 10^{-10} \mathrm{m.s}^{-2}$ determined elsewhere from τ.

Table A3.1: Important galaxy data where valid fits found

1 Fig.	2 Galaxy Name	3 Type	4 Scale Radius a (pub)	5 Newton a (fit)	6 Carmeli a (fit)
A3.2	NGC 3198	SBc	2.5	–	1.85
A3.3	NGC 2903	Sc	1.9	0.31	0.98
A3.4	IC 0342	Sc		0.74	1.05
A3.5	NGC 1097	SBb		0.62	2.12
A3.6	MW Galaxy	Sb		0.12	1.09

Galaxy Name	7 Newton M	8 Carmeli M	9 Newton M_{10}	10 Carmeli M_{10}	11 Ratio
NGC 3198	–	0.984	6.554	0.956	6.85
NGC 2903	0.54	2.12	8.81	2.12	4.16
IC 0342	1.28	1.81	8.2	1.809	4.53
NGC 1097	4.8	9.74	22.997	9.242	2.49
MW Galaxy	0.45	2.31	9.302	2.308	4.03

Note: In cols 4–6, a in units of kpc; in cols 7–10, M in units 10^{10} $M_\odot$; M_{10} is mass calculated at $r = 10$ kpc.

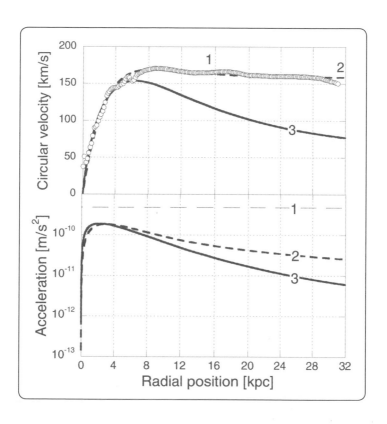

Figure A3.2

(a) Above: the rotational speeds of tracer gases in NGC 3198 (SBc barbed spiral) (circles—curve 1). Theoretical curve fits from the Carmelian equation (A3.16) (broken curve 2) and from the Newtonian equation (A3.9) (curve 3).

(b) Below: the critical acceleration $\frac{2}{3} a_0$ (curve 1). The rotational accelerations determined from the Carmelian (curve 2) and the Newtonian (curve 3) equations with their respective values of a and **M**.

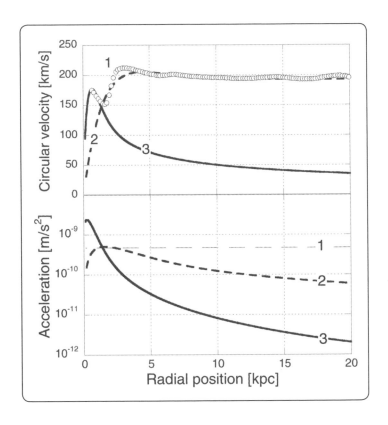

Figure A3.3

(a) **Above: the rotational speeds of tracer gases in NGC 2903 (Sc spiral) (circles—curve 1). Theoretical curve fits from the Carmelian equation (A3.16) (curve 2) and from the Newtonian equation (A3.9) (curve 3).**

(b) **Below: the critical acceleration** $\frac{2}{3}a_0$ **(curve 1). The corresponding rotational accelerations determined from the Carmelian (curve 2) and the Newtonian (curve 3) equations.**

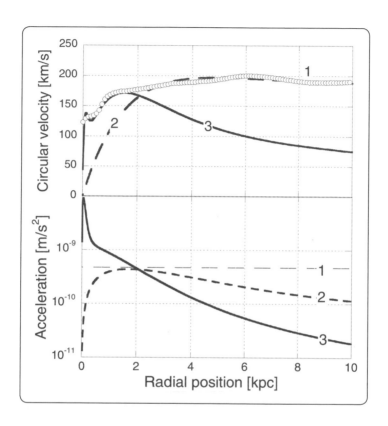

Figure A3.4

(a) Above: the rotational speeds in IC 0342 (Sc spiral) (circles—curve 1). Theoretical curve fits from the Carmelian equation (A3.16) (curve 2) and from the Newtonian equation (A3.9) (curve 3).

(b) Below: the critical acceleration $\frac{2}{3}a_0$ (curve 1). The corresponding rotational accelerations determined from the Carmelian (curve 2) and the Newtonian (curve 3) equations.

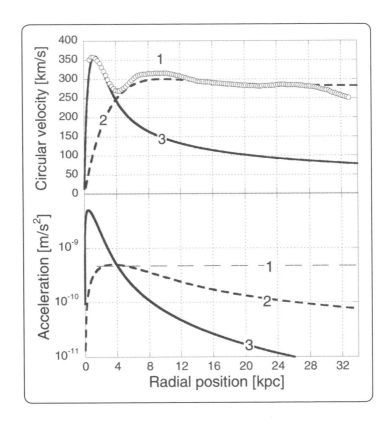

Figure A3.5

(a) Above: the rotational speeds of tracer gases in NGC 1097 (SBb barbed spiral) (circles—curve 1). Theoretical curve fits from the Carmelian equation (A3.16) (curve 2) and from the Newtonian equation (A3.9) (curve 3).

(b) Below: the critical acceleration $\frac{2}{3}a_0$ (curve 1). The corresponding rotational accelerations determined from the Carmelian (curve 2) and the Newtonian (curve 3) equations.

Appendix 3: Spiral galaxy rotation curves explained without dark matter

Extragalactic spirals

The fits to the data for the galaxies shown in figs
A3.2–A3.6 indicate that the new theory works very
well.

In fig. A3.2, showing the barbed spiral NGC 3198,
both Carmelian and Newtonian curve fits were
attempted but only the Carmelian fit (the broken
curve 2) is a good fit. The scale radius $a = 1.85$ kpc
and $M = 0.984 \times 10^{10} \, M_\odot$ were determined from
the fit. Curve 3 shows the best Newtonian fit, with
$a = 2.99$ kpc and $M = 4.2 \times 10^{10} \, M_\odot$, but it doesn't
fit well at high values of r. The Newtonian fit results
in a mass at least 4 times greater than that from the
Carmelian fit. The scale radius determined from
luminous matter for this galaxy is $a = 2.5$ kpc, which
is closer to the Carmelian curve determination.

Fig. A3.2(b) shows that the acceleration using the
Carmelian (curve 2) is dominant and is always less
than the critical acceleration $\frac{2}{3}a_0$. In this model,
when the accelerations are less than the critical
value, the Carmelian force applies. Therefore the
Newtonian force law never applies in this case.

Fig. A3.3 shows the Newtonian and Carmelian
models for the Sc spiral galaxy NGC 2903. In
the high-acceleration regime, a Newtonian fit is
applicable, but when the acceleration drops below
$\frac{2}{3}a_0$, the Carmelian fit applies.

In this and all subsequent top (a) components of each figure, the fits for curves 2 and 3, respectively, apply only for accelerations less than, and greater than, the critical acceleration. In the rotation curve fits, in the top (a) components, the circular velocities are not added, but each applies over its respective regime. This means the masses determined from the Newtonian fits must be less than those from the Carmelian fits, because the Newtonian determined mass must lie within the radius where the two curves cross. The Newtonian fits occur in the stronger acceleration regimes ($> \frac{2}{3} a_0$) close to the galactic centre, as indicated by the bottom (b) figure.

Fig. A3.4 shows the Newtonian and Carmelian models for the Sc spiral galaxy IC 0342 modelled with two central dense Newtonian components. It seems to have a very dense mass concentration toward its centre. The scale radius determined from fits of the innermost component is $a = 0.05$ kpc, while $a = 0.74$ kpc for the outer Newtonian component but $a = 1.05$ kpc for the Carmelian regime. The combined rotation curve is a good fit to the data using the two-acceleration-regime model. Fig. A3.5 shows NGC 1097 modelled with only one central dense Newtonian component. A very good fit is achieved in the Carmelian regime also.

Table A3.1 also shows, in col. 9, the mass (M_{10}) determined at $r = 10$ kpc using the Newtonian formula

$$M = \frac{v^2 r}{G}, \qquad (A3.17)$$

utlizing the measured rotation speeds and assuming that most of the mass is internal to $r = 10$ kpc. This calculation is compared with the mass (M_{10}), in col. 10, derived from the Carmelian equation with $r = 10$ kpc. The ratios of these masses are shown in col. 11. It indicates that using normal Newtonian dynamics seriously overestimates galaxy masses by between 2 and 7 times. These values are consistent with the needed mass levels of halo 'dark' matter to achieve the correct rotation curves.

The Galaxy

Considering the (Milky Way) Galaxy, the same analysis has been applied to the data from ref. 11. See the rotation curve in fig. A3.6(a). Other observers don't record the central peak indicative of a large central mass concentration. However, the compact radio source Sagittarius A* at the Galactic centre is widely believed to be associated with the super-massive black hole with a mass dynamically measured at about $(3.59 \pm 0.59) \times 10^6 \, M_\odot$. Then there is the vast concentration of matter in the Galactic bulge. From the Newtonian curve fit here, we'd expect that within 1.2 kpc of the centre there would be a mass of about $4.5 \times 10^9 \, M_\odot$.

The Carmelian curve fit (curve 2 in fig. A3.6(a)) is an excellent fit over the range 3 to 10 kpc. Except for the intervening region where curves 2 and 3 don't fit the data, the theory works here also. The discrepancy could be due to an unmodelled higher concentration of mass in the central bulge region. Deviations from smooth exponential density decay in the spiral arms are consistent with the oscillations about curve 2 in fig. A3.6(a).

The enclosed mass calculated with $v = 200.78$ km.s^{-1}, the speed of the solar system orbiting the Galactic

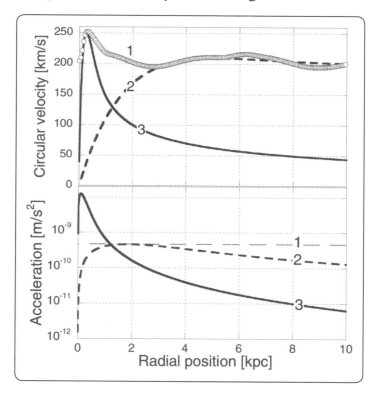

Figure A3.6: (a) Above: the rotational speeds of tracer gases in the Galaxy (Milky Way Sb spiral). Theoretical curve from the Carmelian equation (A3.16) (curve 2) and from the Newtonian equation (A3.9) (curve 3) measured data shown in curve 1.

(b) Below: the critical acceleration $\frac{2}{3}a_0$ (curve 1). The corresponding rotational accelerations determined from the Carmelian (curve 2) and the Newtonian (curve 3) equations respectively.

centre, assumed to be true also at 10 kpc, is
$M_{10} = 9.3 \times 10^{10} M_\odot$ from the Newtonian equation
but $M_{10} = 2.3 \times 10^{10} M_\odot$ from the Carmelian
calculation. This is four times smaller. The distance
of our solar system from the Galactic centre has been
estimated at (7.94 ± 0.42) kpc.[12] At that distance,
the enclosed mass is $M_{10} = 7.6 \times 10^{10} M_\odot$ from the
Newtonian calculation, 3.3 times greater than the
Carmelian calculation.

7. Conclusion

Carmeli's Cosmological General Relativity theory
provides a solution to the rotation curve anomaly
in the outer regions of spiral galaxies without the
need for unseen halo 'dark' matter. Equations of
motion have been derived from Carmeli's five-
dimensional metric, assuming a gravitational potential
in cylindrical coordinates and matter density with
exponential density dependence on the radius. A
Tully–Fisher-type relation results and the rotation
curves for spiral galaxies are accurately reproduced.

Two acceleration regimes were discovered which
were separated by a critical acceleration. For
accelerations larger than the critical value, the
Newtonian force law applies, but for accelerations
less than the critical value, the Carmelian regime
applies. In the Newtonian regime accelerations fall
off as r^{-2} as expected, but in the Carmelian regime
they fall off as r^{-1}. This is new physics but is exactly
what is suggested by Milgrom's phenomenological
MOND theory, only Carmeli provides a theoretical
basis.

References

1. MOND = MOdified Newtonian Dynamics. See Milgrom, M., A modification of the Newtonian dynamics—Implications for galaxies, *Astrophysical Journal* **270**:371–383, 1983; Milgrom, M., A Modification of the Newtonian Dynamics—Implications for Galaxy Systems, *Astrophysical Journal* **270**:384–389, 1983; Milgrom, M., A modification of the Newtonian dynamics as a possible alternative to the hidden mass hypothesis, *Astrophysical Journal* **270**:365–370, 1983.

2. Begeman, K.G., Broeils, A.H. and Sanders R.H., Extended rotation curves of spiral galaxies: Dark haloes and modified dynamics. *M.N.R.A.S.* **249**:523–537, 1991.

3. Carmeli, M., Is galaxy dark matter a property of spacetime? *Int. J. of Theor. Phys.* **37**(10):2621–2625, 1998.

4. Hartnett, J.G., Spiral galaxy rotation curves determined from Carmelian general relativity, *Int. J. Theor. Phys.* **45**(11):2118–2136, 2006. <arxiv.org/abs/astro-ph/0511756>.

5. Toomre, A., On the distribution of matter within highly flattened galaxies, *Ap. J.* **138**:385–392, 1963.

6. Carmeli, M., *Cosmological Special Relativity*, 2nd ed. World Scientific, Singapore, 2002.

7. $M_\odot$ = 1 solar mass unit = 2×10^{30} kg.

8. Hartnett, J.G., The Carmeli metric correctly describes spiral galaxy rotation curves, *Int. J. of Theor. Phys.* **44**(3): 349–362, 2005. <arxiv.org/abs/gr-qc/0407082>.

9. Carmeli, M., Derivation of the Tully–Fisher Law: Doubts about the necessity and existence of halo dark matter, *Int. J. of Theor. Phys.* **39**(5), 1397–1404, 2000.

10. Sofue, Y., Tutui, Y., Honma, H., Tomita, A., Takamiya, T., Koda, J. and Takeda, Y., Central rotationcurves of spiral galaxies, *Ap. J.* **523**:136–146, 1999.

11. Honma, M. and Sofue, Y., Rotation curve of the Galaxy, *Publ. Astron. Soc. Japan* **49**:453, 1997.

12. Eisenhauer, F., Schödel, R., Genzel, R., Ott, T., Tecza, M., Abuter, R., Eckart, A. and Alexander T., A geometric determination of the distance to the galactic center, *Ap. J.* **597**:L121–L124, 2003.

Appendix 4: A finite bounded universe with a unique centre

1. Introduction

This book proposes a model where the Galaxy is at the centre of a spherically symmetric, finite bounded universe. It contends that fits to the magnitude–redshift data of the high-z-type Ia supernovae (SNe Ia)[1] are also consistent with this model; that is, providing that the radius of the universe (a spherically symmetrical matter distribution) is at least $c\tau$, where c is the speed of light and the Hubble–Carmeli constant $\tau \approx 13.54$ Gyr.

This model is based on the CGR theory,[2] but explores the motion of particles in a central potential. In this case, the central potential is the result of the Galaxy being situated at the centre of a spherically symmetric isotropic distribution comprising all matter in the universe.

Appendix 2 (previous chapter) forms the basis of the work presented here. In previous published work,[3,4] the unbounded model was assumed. The reader should at least be familiar with Appendix 2 before proceeding.

As in Appendix 2, we proceed considering only the four coordinates $x^\mu = (x^1, x^2, x^3, x^4)$ $= (r, \theta, \phi, \tau v)^5$—three of space and one of velocity. The parameter τ is the Hubble–Carmeli constant. The

181

usual time dimension is neglected as observations are taken over such a short time period, as though taking a still snapshot, compared to the motion of the galaxies in the universe.

2. Unbounded universe

We write the line element in CGR

$$ds^2 = \tau^2 dv^2 - e^\xi dr^2 - R^2(d\theta^2 + sin^2\theta d\phi^2), \quad (A4.1)$$

which represents a spherically symmetric isotropic universe that is not necessarily homogeneous. Remember, it is fundamental to the theory that, because of the Hubble expansion, the null condition $ds = 0$ is required. (See section 1 of Appendix 1.)

Using spherical coordinates (r, θ, ϕ) and the isotropy condition $d\theta = d\phi = 0$ in (A4.1) then dr represents the radial coordinate distance to the source, and it follows that

$$\tau^2 dv^2 - e^\xi dr^2 = 0, \quad (A4.2)$$

where ξ is a function of v and r alone. This results in

$$\frac{dr}{dv} = \tau e^{-\xi/2}, \quad (A4.3)$$

where the positive sign has been chosen for an expanding universe.

3. Bounded universe—solution in a central potential

Carmeli found a solution to his field equations, modified from Einstein's (see refs. 2 and 6), of the form

$$e^\xi = \frac{R'^2}{1 + f(r)} \qquad\qquad \text{(A4.4)}$$

with $R' = 1$, which must be positive. From the field equations (A2.7)–(A2.9) and (A4.4), we get a differential equation

$$f' + \frac{f}{r} = -\kappa \tau^2 \rho_{eff} r, \qquad\qquad \text{(A4.5)}$$

where $f(r)$ is a function of r and satisfies the condition $1 + f(r) > 0$. The prime is the derivative with respect to r. Here $\kappa = 8\pi\, G/c^2\tau^2$.

The solution of (A4.5), $f(r)$, is the sum of the solution $(2GM/c^2r)$ to the homogeneous equation and a particular solution $(-\kappa\tau^2\rho_{eff}r^2/3)$ to the inhomogeneous equation. Carmeli discarded the homogeneous solution, saying it was not relevant to the universe, but rather the solution of a particle at the origin of coordinates, or, in other words, in a central potential.

Now, suppose we model the universe as a ball of dust of radius Δ, with us, the observers, at the centre of that ball. In this case, the gravitational potential written in spherical coordinates that satisfies Poisson's equation in the Newtonian approximation is

$$\Phi(r) = -\frac{GM}{r} \qquad \text{(A4.6)}$$

for the vacuum solution, but inside an isotropic matter distribution

$$\Phi(r) = -G\left(\frac{4\pi\rho}{r}\int_0^r r'^2\, dr' + 4\pi\rho \int_r^\Delta r'\, dr'\right)$$

$$\text{(A4.7)}$$

$$= \frac{2}{3}G\pi\rho\, r^2 - 2G\pi\rho\, \Delta^2,$$

where it is assumed the matter density ρ is uniform throughout the universe. At the origin ($r = 0$) $\Phi(0) = -2G\pi\rho_m\Delta^2$, where $\rho = \rho_m$, the matter density at the present epoch. In general, ρ depends on epoch. But because we are considering no time development, ρ is only a function of redshift z, and ρ_m can be considered constant.

From (A4.7), it is clear to see that by considering a finite distribution of matter of radial extent Δ, it has the effect of adding a constant to $f(r)$ that is consistent with the constant $2G\pi\rho\, \Delta^2$ in (A4.7), where $f(r)$ is now identified with $-4\Phi/c^2$.

Equation (A4.4)[7] is the solution to (A2.8).[8] More generally, however, (A4.4) can be written as

$$e^{\xi} = \frac{R'^2}{1 + f(r) - K} , \qquad (A4.8)$$

where K is a constant. This is the most general form of the solution of (A2.8). So by substituting (A4.8) into (A2.9) we get the most general form of Carmeli's (A.21)[9]

$$\frac{1}{RR'}(2\dot{R}R' - f') + \frac{1}{R^2}(\dot{R}^2 - f + K) = \kappa \tau^2 \rho_{eff} . \quad (A4.9)$$

Therefore, (A4.8) is also a valid solution of the Einstein field equations in this model. After making the assignment $R = r$, equation (A4.9) yields a more general version of (A4.5); that is,

$$f' + \frac{f - K}{r} = -\kappa \tau^2 \rho_{eff} r . \qquad (A4.10)$$

The solution of (A4.10) is then

$$f(r) = -\frac{1}{3}\kappa \tau^2 \rho_{eff} r^2 + K . \qquad (A4.11)$$

From a comparison with (A4.7) it would seem that the constant K takes the form $K = 8\pi G \rho_{eff}(0)\Delta^2/c^2$, determined from the last term of (A4.7). It is independent of r and describes a non-zero gravitational potential of a finite universe measured at the origin of coordinates. There is some ambiguity, however, as to which density to use in Carmelian cosmology since it is not the same as Newtonian theory. Here, ρ_{eff} is used and evaluated at $r = 0$.

In the above treatment, we have initially assumed that the universe has expanded over time, and at any given epoch it has an averaged density ρ, and hence ρ_{eff}. The solution of the field equations has been sought on this basis. However, because the Carmeli metric is solved in an instant of time (on a cosmological scale), any time-dependence is neglected. In fact, the general time-dependent solution has not yet been found. But since we observe the expanding universe with the coordinates of Hubble at each epoch (or redshift z), we see the universe with a different density $\rho(z)$ and an effective density $\rho_{eff}(z)$. Carmeli arrived at his solution with the constant density assumption. I have made the implicit assumption that the solution is also valid if we allow the density to vary as a function of redshift, as is expected with expansion.

It follows from (A4.3), (A4.8) and (A4.11) that

$$\frac{dr}{dv} = \tau\sqrt{1+\left(\frac{1-\Omega}{c^2\tau^2}\right)r^2}, \qquad (A4.12)$$

where $\Omega = \rho/\rho_c$. This compares with the solution when the central potential is neglected (i.e. $\Delta \to 0$). In fact, the result is identical, as we would expect in a universe where the Hubble Law is universally true.

Therefore (A4.12) may be integrated exactly and yields the same result as Carmeli,

$$\frac{r}{c\tau} = \frac{\sinh(\frac{v}{c}\sqrt{1-\Omega})}{\sqrt{1-\Omega}}. \qquad (A4.13)$$

Since observations in the distant cosmos are always in terms of redshift, z, we write (A4.13) as a function of redshift where r is expressed in units of $c\tau$ and $v/c = ((1 + z)^2 - 1)/((1 + z)^2 + 1)$ from the relativistic Doppler formula. The latter is appropriate since this is a velocity dimension.

What is important to note, though, is that regardless of the geometry of the universe, provided it is spherically symmetrical and isotropic on the large scale, (A4.13) is identical to that which we would get where the universe has a unique centre, with one difference, which is explored in the following section. For an isotropic universe without a unique centre, one can have an arbitrary number of centres. However, if we are currently in a universe where the Galaxy is at the centre of the local isotropy distribution, this means the universe we see must be very large and we are currently limited from seeing into an adjacent region with a different isotropy centre.

4. Gravitational redshift

In Appendix 2, the geometry of that model is the usual unbounded type, as found in an infinite universe, for example. In a finite bounded universe, one must consider an additional effect on the photons being received from the distant sources. The gravitational redshift (z_{grav}) resulting from the Galaxy sitting *at the unique centre of a finite spherically symmetric matter distribution* must be considered. In this case we need to consider the difference in gravitational potential between the points of emission and reception of a photon. Now the 00th metric component, the time part of the 5D metric of coordinates $x^{\mu} = (ct, r, \theta, \phi, \tau v)$ where $\mu = 0,1,2,3,4$, is required, but it has never been determined for the cosmos in the Carmelian theory. In general relativity we would relate it by $g_{00} = 1 - 4\Phi/c^2$, where -4Φ is the gravitational potential. The factor 4 and the minus sign arise from the Carmelian theory when (A4.11) and (A4.7) are compared. So the question must be answered, "What is the g_{00} metric component for the large scale structure of the universe in CGR?"

First note from (A4.4) and (A4.5) that the g_{11} metric component (considered in an unbounded universe for the moment) is

$$g_{11} = -\left(1 + \frac{1-\Omega}{c^2\tau^2}r^2\right)^{-1} \qquad \text{(A4.14)}$$

in CGR. Also we can write a scale radius

$$R_0 = \frac{c\tau}{\sqrt{|1-\Omega|}}. \qquad \text{(A4.15)}$$

Hence we can define an energy density from the curvature

$$\Omega_K = \frac{c^2}{h^2 R_0^2} = \frac{c^2 \tau^2}{R_0^2} \, , \qquad (A4.16)$$

which, when we use (A4.15), becomes

$$\Omega_K = 1 - \Omega \, . \qquad (A4.17)$$

In the FRW theory the energy density of the cosmological constant is defined $\rho_\Lambda = \Lambda/8\pi G$, hence

$$\Omega_\Lambda = \frac{\Lambda}{3H_0^2} \, . \qquad (A4.18)$$

Even though the cosmological constant is not explicitly used in CGR, it follows from the definition of the critical density that

$$\rho_c = \frac{3}{8\pi G \tau^2} = \frac{\Lambda}{8\pi G} \, , \qquad (A4.19)$$

when the cosmological constant Λ is identified with $3/\tau^2$. Therefore in CGR it follows that

$$\Omega_\Lambda = \frac{\Lambda}{3h^2} = \Lambda \left(\frac{\tau^2}{3} \right) = 1 \, . \qquad (A4.20)$$

This means that in CGR the vacuum energy $\rho_{vac} = \Lambda/8\pi G$ is encoded in the metric via the critical density since $\rho_{eff} = \rho - \rho_c$ principally defines the physics. So $\Omega_\Lambda = 1$ identically and at all epochs of time. (The determination of Ω_Λ in ref. 3 was flawed due to an incorrect definition.) Also we can relate Ω_Λ to the curvature energy density by

$$\Omega_K = \Omega_\Lambda - \Omega, \qquad \text{(A4.21)}$$

which becomes

$$\Omega_k = \Omega_\Lambda - \Omega_m, \qquad \text{(A4.22)}$$

at the present epoch ($z \approx 0$). Here $\Omega = \Omega_m(1 + z)^3$ and hence $\Omega_K \to \Omega_k$ as $z \to 0$. Finally we can write for the total energy density, the sum of the matter density and the curvature density,

$$\Omega_t = \Omega + \Omega_K = \Omega + 1 - \Omega = 1, \qquad \text{(A4.23)}$$

which means the present epoch value is trivially

$$\Omega_0 = \Omega_m + \Omega_k = \Omega_m + 1 - \Omega_m = 1. \quad \text{(A4.24)}$$

This means that the 3D spatial part of the universe is always flat as it expands. This explains why we live in a universe that we observe to be identically geometrically spatially flat. The curvature is due to the velocity dimension. Only at some past epoch, in a radiation dominated universe, would the total mass/energy density depart from unity.

Now considering a finite bounded universe, from (A4.11), I therefore write g_{00} as

$$g_{00}(r) = 1 + (1 - \Omega_t)\frac{r^2}{c^2\tau^2} + 3(\Omega_t - 1)\frac{\Delta^2}{c^2\tau^2} . \quad \text{(A4.25)}$$

Equation (A4.25) follows from $g_{00} = 1 - 4\Phi/c^2$ where Φ is taken from the gravitational potential but with effective density, which in turn involves the total energy density because we are now considering *spacetime*.

Clearly from (A4.23) it follows that $g_{00}(r) = 1$ regardless of epoch. Thus from the usual relativistic expression

$$1 + z_{grav} = \sqrt{\frac{g_{00}(0)}{g_{00}(r)}} = 1, \quad \text{(A4.26)}$$

and the gravitational redshift is zero regardless of epoch. As expected, if the emission and reception of a photon both occur in flat space then we'd expect no gravitational effects.

In an unbounded universe, though no gravitational effects need be considered, the result, $g_{00} = 1$ is also the same. Therefore we can write down the full 5D line element for CGR in any dynamic spherically symmetrical isotropic universe,

$$ds^2 = c^2 dt^2 - \left(1 + \frac{1 - \Omega}{c^2\tau^2}r^2\right)^{-1} dr^2 + \tau^2 dv^2 . \quad \text{(A4.27)}$$

The θ and ϕ coordinates do not appear due to the isotropy condition $d\theta = d\phi = 0$. Due to the Hubble Law the 2nd and 3rd terms sum to zero leaving

$dt = ds/c$, the proper time. Clocks, co-moving with the galaxies in the Hubble expansion, would measure the same proper time.

Since it follows from (A4.25) that $g_{00}(r) = 1$ regardless of epoch, $g_{00}(r)$ is not sensitive to any value of Δ, the radius of the universe. This means the above analysis is true regardless of whether the universe is bounded or unbounded. The observations cannot distinguish the two. In an unbounded or bounded universe of any type no gravitational redshift (due to cosmological causes) in light from distant source galaxies would be observed.

However, inside the Galaxy we expect the matter density to be much higher than critical, i.e. $\Omega_{galaxy} \gg 1$, and the total mass/energy density can be written

$$\Omega_0 \big|_{galaxy} = \Omega_{galaxy} + \Omega_k \approx \Omega_{galaxy} , \quad (A4.28)$$

because $\Omega_k \approx 1$, since it is cosmologically determined. Therefore this explains why only the galaxy matter density is appropriate when considering the Poisson equation for galaxies.[10]

As a result inside a galaxy we can write

$$g_{00}(r) = 1 + \Omega_K \frac{r^2}{c^2\tau^2} + \Omega_{galaxy} \frac{r^2}{c^2\tau^2} , \quad (A4.29)$$

in terms of densities at some past epoch. Depending on the mass density of the galaxy, or cluster of galaxies, the value of g_{00} here changes. As we approach larger and larger structures the mass density approaches that of the universe as a whole and $g_{00} \rightarrow 1$ as we approach the largest scales of the universe. Galaxies in the cosmos then act only as local perturbations but have no effect on Ω_K. That depends only on the average mass density of the whole universe, which depends on epoch (z).

Equation (A4.30) below is in essence the same expression used by Carmeli[11] in his gravitational redshift formula rewritten here as

$$\frac{\lambda_2}{\lambda_1} = \sqrt{\frac{1 + \Omega_K \, r_2^2 / c^2 \tau^2 - R_S / r_2}{1 + \Omega_K \, r_1^2 / c^2 \tau^2 - R_S / r_1}} \,, \quad (A4.30)$$

involving a cosmological contribution ($\Omega_K \, r^2/c^2\tau^2$) and $R_S = 2GM/c^2$, a local contribution where the mass M is that of a compact object. The curvature (Ω_K) results from the averaged mass/energy density of the whole cosmos, which determines how the galaxies 'move', but motions of particles within galaxies are dominated by the mass of the galaxy and the masses of the compact objects within. Therefore when considering the gravitational redshifts due to compact objects we can neglect any cosmological effects, only the usual Schwarzschild radius of the object need be considered. The cosmological contributions in (A4.30) are generally negligible. This then leads back to the realm of general relativity.

5. White hole

Now if we assume that the radial extent of a finite matter distribution at the current epoch is equal to the current epoch scale radius, we can write

$$\Delta = \frac{1}{\sqrt{\Omega_k}} = \frac{1}{\sqrt{1-\Omega_m}} , \qquad (A4.31)$$

expressed in units of $c\tau$. In such a case, $\Delta = 1.02\ c\tau$ if $\Omega_m = 0.04$ and $\Delta = 1.01\ c\tau$ if $\Omega_m = 0.02$.

It is important to note also that Carmeli's unbounded model (A4.13) describes the redshift distance relationship, but there is no central potential. In refs 3 and 4, equation (A4.13) was the curve fitted to the SNe Ia data and was found to agree with $0.02 \le \Omega_m \le 0.04$ without the inclusion of 'dark' matter or 'dark' energy. Therefore, the same conclusion must also apply to the finite bounded model here.

In order to achieve a fit to the data, using either the unbounded or the bounded model, the white hole solution of equation (A4.5) or (A4.10) must be chosen respectively. The sign of the terms in (A4.11), means that the gravitational potential implicit in (A4.11) is a potential hill,[12] not a potential well. Therefore, the (finite) bounded solution describes an expanding white hole with the observer at the origin of the coordinates, the unique centre of the universe determined by Δ. This solution can only be rejected philosophically. Using the Carmeli theory, the observational data cannot distinguish between finite bounded models ($\infty > \Delta \ge c\tau$) and finite ($\Delta = 0$) or infinite ($\Delta = \infty$) unbounded models.

The physical meaning is that the solution, developed here, represents an expanding white hole centred on our galaxy. The galaxies in the universe are spherically symmetrically distributed around the Galaxy. The observed redshifts are the result of cosmological expansion alone.

Moreover, if we assume $\Delta \approx c\,\tau$, then it can be shown[4] that the Schwarzschild radius for the finite universe

$$R_S \approx \Omega_m \Delta = 0.04\ c\tau. \qquad \text{(A4.32)}$$

Therefore, for a universe with $\Delta \approx c\tau$ it follows that $R_s > 0.04\ c\tau \approx 200$ Mpc. An expanding finite bounded universe can be considered to be a white hole. As the universe continues to expand, the matter enclosed within the Schwarzschild radius gets less and less. The gravitational radius of that matter therefore shrinks towards the earth at the centre.

This is similar to the theoretical result obtained by Smoller and Temple,[13] who constructed a new cosmology from the FRW metric but with a shock wave causing a time reversal white hole. In their model, the total mass behind the shock decreases as the shock wave, which is spherically symmetrically centred on the Galaxy, expands. Their paper states in part '... the entropy condition implies that the shock wave must weaken to the point where it settles down to an Oppenheimer Snyder interface (bounding a finite total mass), that eventually emerges from the white hole event horizon of an ambient Schwarzschild spacetime.'

This result then implies that the earth, or at least the Galaxy, is in fact close to the physical centre of the universe. Smoller and Temple[14] state that 'With a shock wave present, the *Copernican Principle is violated* in the sense that the earth then has a special position relative to the shock wave. But of course, in these shock wave refinements of the FRW metric, there is a spacetime on the other side of the shock wave, beyond the galaxies, and so the scale of uniformity of the FRW metric, the scale on which the density of the galaxies is uniform, is no longer the largest length scale. [emphasis added]'

Their shock wave refinement of a critically expanding FRW metric leads to a big bang universe of finite total mass. The model presented here also has a finite total mass and is a spatially flat universe. It describes a finite bounded white hole that started expanding at some time in the past.

6. Conclusion

Since the Carmeli theory has been successfully analyzed with distance modulus data derived by the high-z-type Ia supernova teams, it must also be consistent with a universe that places the Galaxy at the centre of a spherically symmetric, isotropic, expanding white hole of finite radius. The result describes particles moving in both a central potential and an accelerating, expanding white hole universe without the need for the inclusion of 'dark' matter. The data cannot be used to exclude models with finite extensions $\Delta \geq c\tau$.

References

1. See Appendix 2.
2. Carmeli, M., *Cosmological Special Relativity*, 2nd ed. World Scientific, Singapore, 2002.
3. Hartnett, J.G., The distance modulus determined from Carmeli's cosmology fits the accelerating universe data of the high-redshift type Ia supernovae without dark matter, *Found. Phys.* **36**(6):839–861, 2006. <arxiv.org/abs/astro-ph/0501526>.
4. Oliveira, F.J. and Hartnett, J.G., Carmeli's cosmology fits data for an accelerating and decelerating universe without dark matter or dark energy, *Found. Phys. Lett.* **19**(6):519–535, 2006. <arxiv.org/abs/astro-ph/0603500>.
5. The zeroth coordinate is time $x^0 = ct$.
6. Behar, S. and Carmeli, M., Cosmological relativity: A new theory of cosmology, *Int. J. Theor. Phys.* **39**(5):1375–1396, 2000.
7. Carmeli's equation (A.19), from p. 123 of ref. 2.
8. Carmeli's equation (A.17), from p. 122 of ref. 2.
9. Ref. 2, p. 123.
10. Toomre, A., On the distribution of matter within highly flattened galaxies, *Ap. J.* **138**:385–392, 1963.
11. Ref. 2, p. 173.
12. Caution is needed when comparing to *spacetime* as this potential hill is only relevant to *spacevelocity*.
13. Smoller, J. and Temple, B. *PNAS* **100**(20):11216–11218, 2003.
14. Smoller, J. and Temple, B., <www.math.ucdavis.edu/ temple/ articles/temple1234.pdf>.

Appendix 5: The Galaxy at the centre of concentric spherical shells of galaxies

1. Introduction

Humphreys' white hole cosmology involved effects that resulted from Einstein's general relativity where the usual assumptions on boundary conditions were changed.[1] In his case, he chose a finite bounded universe, instead of the usually assumed unbounded model. His model was, however, four-dimensional. In this book I have assumed similar boundary conditions but a five-dimensional universe.[2] The model chosen is that of Israeli theoretical physicist Moshe Carmeli, which is extensively explained in either of his books titled *Cosmological Special Relativity*[3] or *Cosmological Relativity.*[4]

Carmelian cosmology is based on the idea that the Hubble Law is fundamental to the universe. This means that not only do we have the usual three space dimensions and one time dimension, but also a new dimension that quantifies the velocity of the expansion of space. We see the universe expanding on the largest scales. Therefore the assumption means that it is the fabric of space that is expanding and the galaxies are going along for the ride. And astronomers measure only distance and velocity in the expanding universe. Distance is determined from the brightness or magnitude of the sources and velocity from their redshifts. From this approach we will see, in Appendix 6, a solution to the starlight travel-time problem.

But questions may be asked: 'So, what is the shape of the universe?' and, 'Is it valid to use the solution of Einstein's field equations in the Carmelian theory with the assumption that we are observers at the centre of the physical universe characterized by an isotropic distribution of matter?' If it could be shown that the matter distribution was homogeneous, then the solution would still hold, but the assumption of uniqueness would not.

2. What do we observe in the universe?

Do we see a homogeneous distribution of matter? This is a very difficult question to answer, because the usual method of measuring the distances to large collections of very distant galaxies relies on the Hubble Law. And the exact form of the Hubble Law at high redshift (i.e. large distances) depends heavily on the particular details of the assumed cosmological model.

Nevertheless there have been a couple of large-scale mapping projects that take a slice of the heavens and project it onto a plane. The 2dF Galaxy Redshift Survey (2dFGRS),[5] a joint UK–Australian project, sampled about two hundred thousand galaxies in 2-degree slices above and below the plane of the

Figure A5.1: Galaxy number density (N) as a function of redshift (z) from the SDSS survey. Bin size Δz = 0.001. Only 20,000 galaxies were used in the analysis. The solid curve is a smooth polynomial fit that ignores the peaks.

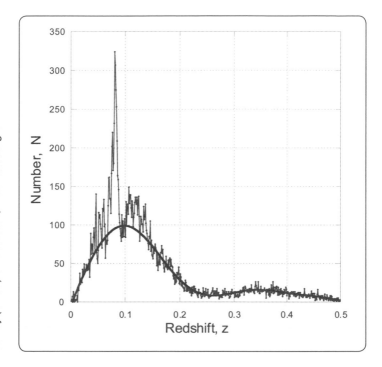

Astrophysical Research Consortium (ARC) and the Sloan Digital Sky Survey (SDSS) Collaboration, <www.sdss.org>.

Galaxy. Fig. 5.3 (in the main text) shows a map of the measured galaxies as a function of distance from the apex, which represents the observer on Earth. Another, the Sloan Digital Sky Survey (SDSS),[6] in 2003 announced the first measurements of galactic structures more than a billion light-years across and mapped about two hundred thousand galaxies in 6% of the sky. This would mean slices of about 21-degree thickness. A portion of these galaxies is shown in fig. 5.4 (in the main text), projected onto a plane.

It would appear from these maps that the assumption of homogeneity cannot be supported. Fig. 5.4 (only a portion of the data) and the left side of fig. 5.3 show not only concentric but also circular structures centred on our galaxy more clearly than do earlier maps. This result is more than an artefact of the sampling technique because the density distribution of galaxies is expected to increase with distance in a big bang universe, as one looks back in time, until an expected decrease in number is observed due to the fact that the galaxies get too dim to be seen. In these maps, the galaxy density seems to oscillate (decrease and increase periodically) with distance, hence the circular structures. This spatial galaxy density variation can result from the fact that galaxies are preferentially found at certain discrete distances.

Detailed analysis

Let us analyze this further and count the number of galaxies (N) in a redshift slice (Δz) as a function of redshift z. On the 2dFGRS website we see a plot[7] of galaxy number density (N) as a function of redshift (z). It shows the expected increase in galaxy count as a function of redshift due to the increase in surface area as larger areas are taken into account with redshift. Then we see the expected decrease in number count due to galaxies becoming dimmer as a result of the inverse square law of illumination.

If the counts are taken from a thin slice, as is the case in these surveys, we expect the count to increase approximately linearly with redshift. When 20,000 galaxies from the SDSS were analyzed (see fig.A5.1) a similar plot of N vs z resulted where the data are binned with $\Delta z = 0.001$. The increase in N is linear to $z = 0.06$ after which it is difficult to determine due to the massive spike in number density at $z = 0.08$. The SDSS data used here was mostly sampled close to the plane of the ecliptic, certainly within ± 10 degrees, so we'd expect the redshift z-dependence of N to be a power law z^n, where $1 < n < 2$. This is qualitatively indicated.

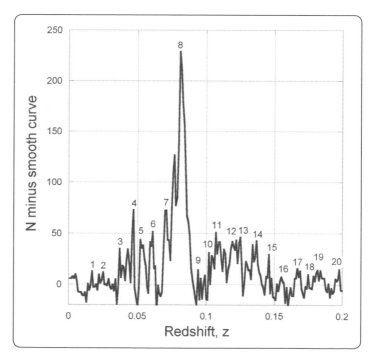

Figure A5.2: Galaxy number density (N) as function of redshift (z) from fig. A5.1, where the smooth polynomial curve has been removed. Period structure indicates the preferred distances from the earth at which the galaxies are located.

Discrete redshifts

There are a number of prominent spikes seen in the
N vs z plots from the 2dFGRS and SDSS data (see
fig. A5.1 for SDSS) indicating preferred distances
for galaxies, where they tend to concentrate. This is
strongly indicative of the concentric structure we see
in figs 5.3 and 5.4 in the main text. In fig. A5.1, here,
I have fitted a smooth polynomial curve to the data,
indicating the initial rise in number density and then
the fall-off due to the sources becoming too dim to be
seen. The only unexpected feature there is the second
rise and fall.

Then by subtracting off the polynomial, the density
oscillations are more clearly seen. These are shown
in fig. A5.2. There are clear peaks at 0.037, 0.047,
0.054, 0.061, 0.071, 0.081, 0.093, 0.102, 0.108 with
others above and below these. In fig. A5.2 I have
attempted to label all the visible peaks. Their redshifts
are plotted against peak number in fig. A5.3. Then
these peaks are fitted with a linear dependence on
peak number (broken line in fig. A5.3) resulting in
an average separation of 0.00919 ± 0.00003 with an
offset 0.0082. This interval amounts to a separation
of approximately 36 Mpc (about one hundred
million light-years). This then tells us that we are in
a galactocentric universe with galaxies preferentially
piled up with this spacing—and most significantly
at $z = 0.081$, which is a radial distance of about
320 Mpc, or about one billion light-years, from us at
the centre. Each peak then represents the preferred
location of the galaxies that lie on spherically
concentric shells centred on our galaxy.

Notice also that in fig. A5.3, the initial offset is actually somewhere between 0.008 and 0.009, because I assigned the redshift value to a Δz bin by its starting redshift, that is, the bin covers the interval $(z, z + \Delta z)$. Therefore the initial ring of galaxies should begin at approximately $z = 0.0085 \pm 0.0005$, but only a small peak is visible at $z = 0.005$ in fig. A5.2 and no peak at all near $z = 0.008$ to 0.009. Notice also that in fig. A5.3 I have plotted peaks above number 20 of fig. A5.2, taken from fig. A5.5. The constant spacing no longer holds where $z > 0.2$. However, we don't expect the simple Hubble Law

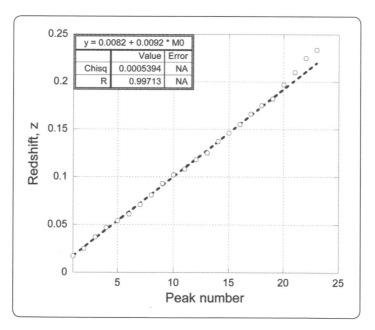

Figure A5.3: The redshift of the peaks in fig. A5.2 plotted as a function of the peak number. The broken curve is the best fit line determined from peak data up to 20. In this case the best fit interval between peaks is 0.00919 ± 0.00003 with an offset of 0.0082.

linear dependence ($cz = H_0 r$) to apply beyond $z = 0.2$ either.

I took a sample of 20,000 quasars (or QSOs) from the SDSS data set and the resulting N vs z plot is shown in fig. A5.4, where the data have been binned with $\Delta z = 0.01$. Again we see clear peaks; what is most significant is that there are regions of redshift where no QSOs are observed at all. If the redshifts for QSOs are interpreted as the result of the Hubble Law, which I contend is very much debatable,[8] then these data also describe more concentric shells around our Galaxy where the quasars are preferentially located. See fig. A5.5, where I have combined the number count for QSOs and galaxies with data that has been binned with $\Delta z = 0.001$. Fig. A5.5 is shown with a log scale on the z-axis. From this we see that the galaxies dominate at low redshift and the QSOs at high redshift, because few galaxies are reported in the sample with $z > 0.5$.

In fig. A5.4 I have labelled the peaks that are observed in the redshift distribution of QSOs and plotted the peak redshifts against peak number in fig. A5.6. It is found, by forcing a linear fit through the origin, that the resulting approximately constant redshift interval between peaks is 0.262 ± 0.003, but when not forced through the origin, the best fit interval is 0.270 ± 0.005 and the offset is -0.055. The former has a smaller standard error and so that is adopted. The problem then is to interpret the meaning of this interval.

However without making any interpretation it is obvious that the Galaxy lies at the centre of a giant isotropic distribution of quasars in redshift parameter space. This cannot be a coincidence. If the Galaxy was randomly located in the universe we'd expect no particular spacing or any spacing in peaks at all. And if the redshifts for quasars are to be interpreted as resulting from their enormous recession speed in an expanding universe (hence they follow the Hubble Law, and are more distant with greater redshift), then why are not less of them visible following a general trend as a function of redshift? We only start to see

Astrophysical Research Consortium (ARC) and the Sloan Digital Sky Survey (SDSS) Collaboration, <www.sdss.org>.

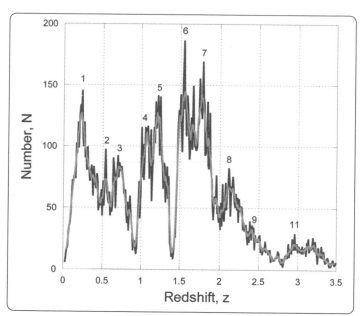

Figure A5.4: QSO number density (N) as a function of redshift (z) from the SDSS survey. Bin size $\Delta z = 0.01$. Only 20,000 QSOs were used in the analysis.

Figure A5.5: Combined 20,000 galaxy and 20,000 QSO number density (N) as a function of redshift (z) from figs A5.4 and A5.6 on a log scale. Bin size $\Delta z = 0.001$. QSOs dominate the high-redshift region while galaxy numbers dominate at low redshift.

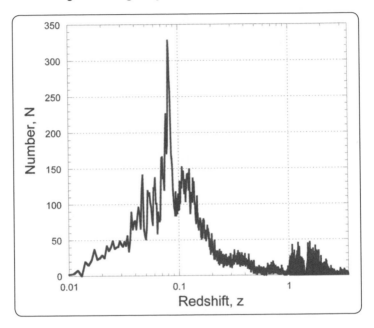

this type of effect occurring beyond $z = 2$. But for $z <$ 2 we see oscillations in number (N).

However, what is interesting is that peak number 23 of fig. A5.3 for galaxies corresponds with peak number 1 of fig. A5.6 for QSOs. It will be seen below that a case can be argued for the low-redshift quasars being more galaxy-like than the high-redshift ones. Therefore the redshift we are observing for these should correspond to that resulting from the expansion of the cosmos,[9] and hence contain no large intrinsic component. Therefore the redshift of peak

Figure A5.6: The redshift of the peaks in fig. A5.4 plotted as a function of the peak number. The broken curve is the best fit line, where the curve is forced through the origin. In this case the best fit interval between peaks is 0.262 ± 0.003, but when not forced through the origin, the best fit interval is 0.270 ± 0.005 and the offset is −0.055.

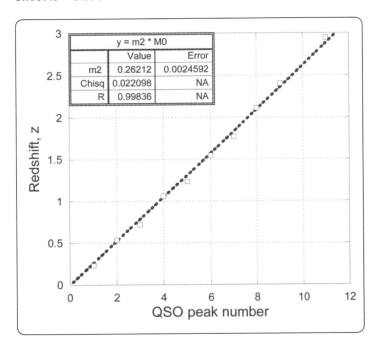

number 1, from figs A5.4 and A5.6, is assumed to be totally due to the expansion of the cosmos. This then links the galaxies with the quasars.

Redshift–distance modulus

If we analyze the apparent magnitudes of the galaxies in our sample, see fig. A5.7, we notice that the brightest galaxies (lowest magnitude value) form a clear line that closely follows the distance modulus versus redshift dependence derived from the Carmeli–Hartnett theory.[10] In fig. A5.7 the solid black curve is the magnitude–distance modulus taken from Appendix 2 with the present epoch matter density $\Omega_m = 0.04$ and the Hubble–Carmeli constant $h = 72.17$ km.s^{-1} Mpc^{-1}. The curve has been scaled by the addition of -24 magnitudes, which represents the reference (fiducial) absolute magnitude of the brightest galaxy in the group for a given redshift value. This curve is the result of fitting the Carmeli theory to the high-redshift-supernova-distance-modulus data, and successfully describes the expanding universe without the need to include 'dark' matter or 'dark' energy.

The way to understand fig. A5.7 is with an analogy using random groups of people. If we take each group of galaxies at a given redshift, then we would expect that the brightest galaxy (with smallest apparent magnitude) in each group would have about the same intrinsic brightness or absolute magnitude. This assumes that all galaxies are essentially formed the same way. As with random groups of people, we would expect that the tallest person in each group would be about the same height.

Therefore, from the analysis in fig. A5.7 we see, by scaling the fitting curve by an unknown absolute-magnitude value for the brightest galaxy, we get a pretty good fit. (It merely shifts the curve up or down the Magnitude axis.) There is a slight departure at low redshifts, but this can be accounted for if we assume that the higher the redshift of the object, the younger the galaxy, due to the finite travel time of the

Figure A5.7: Apparent magnitude (i band) as a function of redshift for the 20,000 sampled galaxies (grey dots) of SDSS. The solid black curve is the magnitude-distance modulus taken from the Carmeli–Hartnett theory with the present epoch matter density Ω_m = 0.04 and the Hubble–Carmeli constant h = 72.17 km.s^{-1} Mpc^{-1}. The curve has been scaled by the addition of -24 magnitudes, which represents the reference-absolute-magnitude of the brightest galaxy in the group at any one redshift value.

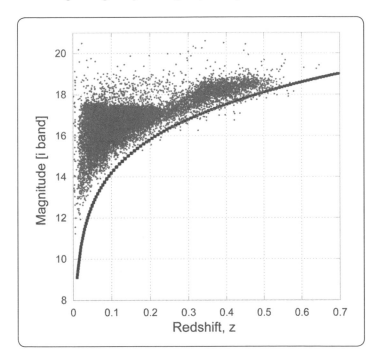

light. This means that the more distant galaxies are seen at a slightly earlier stage of their development and consequently may be brighter. In the high-z supernova studies such an effect is corrected for.

Therefore the data here is telling us that the Hubble Law works quite well for the galaxies. But what about the quasars? Fig. A5.8 plots the same galaxy sample as in fig. A5.7 but includes all the QSOs in the sample that have redshifts $z < 0.7$. Notice that in this case even the low-redshift quasars, where $z < 0.4$, also seem to lie above the fit line for the brightest galaxies. But for $z > 0.4$ there seems to be no correspondence with the theory.

Fig. A5.9 plots the apparent magnitude of the whole sample set of 20,000 QSOs against redshift. Each QSO is a black dot. Most of the data fall on the right of the solid black fitted curve. To follow the Hubble Law they must fall on the left of it. This is strong evidence that quasar redshifts are, in fact, not totally due to the expansion of the cosmos, but contain some intrinsic component as suggested by Arp and others.[11]

Fig. A5.9 also compares the apparent magnitude with the number (N) of the QSOs in the sample over the same redshift-parameter space. It can be clearly seen that the absences of the data points correspond to strong dips in $N(z)$. There are preferred redshift values for the quasars and also, it seems, forbidden redshifts. This further strengthens the argument that QSOs lie at discrete redshifts but that these are not Hubble Law or distance-determining redshifts.

Possibly, as suggested by others, there is a smaller contribution that is the expansion-redshift component on top of a dominant intrinsic component due to their youth. Then the higher-redshift QSOs are younger— we are seeing them closer to their moment of creation.

Now let us use

$$1 + z_c = \frac{1 + z_{obs}}{1 + z_i} \qquad (A5.1)$$

to calculate the redshift (z_c) of the QSO assuming that its redshift is dominated by an intrinsic component (z_i). The calculated redshift z_c may also be a combination of Doppler, due to the quasar being ejected from a host galaxy, and expansion redshift, which

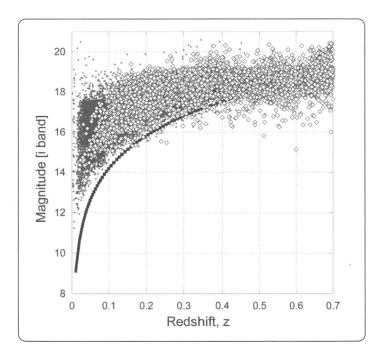

Figure A5.8: Apparent magnitude (i band) as a function of redshift for all the sampled galaxies (grey dots) of fig. A5.7 and the QSOs (open diamonds) with redshifts $z < 0.7$. The solid black curve is the same magnitude-distance-modulus curve as in fig. A5.7.

Figure A5.9: Apparent magnitude (i band) as a function of redshift for all the 20,000 sampled QSOs (black dots) of SDSS. The solid black curve is the same magnitude-distance modulus curve as in fig. A5.7. The broken curve is the N vs z curve with bin $\Delta z = 0.05$. Note the correspondence between the absence of quasars and the curve minima.

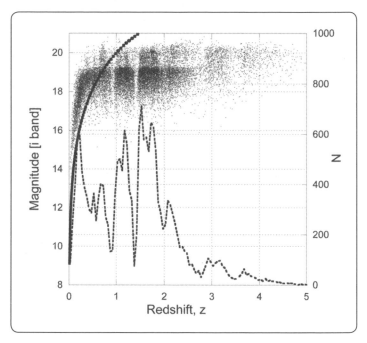

is due to the cosmological expansion of the cosmos. Here z_{obs} are the observed values of the redshift peaks. To the QSO peak data of fig. A5.6, shown in table A5.1, column 2, I applied equation (A5.1) using Karlsson's preferred values,[12] listed in column 3, for z_i, and obtained the calculated redshift values shown in column 4. The resulting values can easily be made to accord with the lower-redshift peaks of the galaxies seen in fig. A5.2, if we include small Doppler contributions to the redshift of the order of ± 0.005.

Table A5.1: Redshift abundance peak values from SDSS QSO data

Peak #	QSO peak redshift	Karlsson's values	Calculated redshift
1	0.233	0.00	0.233
2	0.535	0.30	0.181
3	0.719	0.60	0.056
4	1.059	0.96	0.051
5	1.235	0.96	0.13
6	1.546	1.41	0.056
7	1.770	1.41	0.149
8	2.109	1.96	0.050
9	2.401	1.96	0.149
10			
11	2.946	2.63	0.087

This is entirely reasonable in light of observations of high-redshift quasars being seen ejected from the nucleus of active galaxies.[13] A Doppler contribution of 0.005 is, after all, only 0.5% of the speed of light and for an astronomical ejection process this is indeed very small.

The above analysis is telling us something quite significant. Though more research is needed, it is clear from the data that we live in a galactocentric universe. We are located in a special place. The universe we see is isotropic in the distribution of galaxies and quasars; it is definitely not homogeneous. Spherical symmetry, that is isotropy, is the fundamental assumption in the Carmeli theory, but the Friedmann–Lemaitre (FL) theory requires that it be homogeneous as well. Therefore the FL theory cannot be applied under these circumstances but Carmeli's theory is perfectly valid.

Conclusion

The Carmelian cosmology is framed in an isotropic, yet not necessarily homogeneous, universe, and one solution of Einstein's field equations that it permits is that of a finite expanding white hole with the Galaxy at the centre. Observations from the large galaxy surveys seem to indicate that we do indeed live at the centre of concentric spherical shells of galaxies with a spacing of about one hundred million light-years.

Also, observations indicate that quasars are distributed at discrete redshifts, and if Arp, Burbidge and others[14] are right, this means those quasars are much closer than their redshift distances would indicate. Hence it follows that they are distributed on concentric spherical shells, along with the galaxies. Therefore it is not only valid to apply the Carmelian cosmology—what we observe seems to be consistent with a biblical description of the universe.

The universe was made for a purpose—we are placed here at the centre to observe the Lord's glorious creation all around us.

References

1. Humphreys, D.R., *Starlight and Time* Master Books, Colorado Springs, 1994; Humphreys, D.R., New vistas of space and time, *J. of Creation* **12**(2):195–212, 1998.
2. With the exception of the 'waters above', I don't postulate that they form the edge of the finite sphere of galaxies as Humphreys does.
3. Carmeli, M., *Cosmological Special Relativity*, 2nd ed. World Scientific, Singapore, 2002.
4. Carmeli, M., *Cosmological Relativity*, World Scientific, Singapore, 2006.
5. <www.aao.gov.au/2df>.
6. <www.sdss.org>.
7. <www.mso.anu.edu.au/2dFGRS>.
8. Hartnett, J.G., Quantized quasar redshifts in a creationist cosmology, *J. of Creation* **18**(2):105–113, 2004; Hartnett, J.G., The heavens declare a different story! *J. of Creation* **17**(2):94–97, 2003.
9. See Repp, A.S., The nature of redshifts and an argument by Gentry, *CRSQ* **39**:269–274, December 2002, for a good discussion about different types of redshift.
10. See Appendix 2 and my papers cited there.
11. Arp, H., *Seeing Red: redshifts, cosmology and academic science*, Apeiron, Montreal, 1998.
12. Karlsson, K.G., On the existence of significant peaks in the quasar redshift distribution, *A&A* **58**:237–240, 1977; Hartnett, J.G., Quantized quasar redshifts in a creationist cosmology, *J. of Creation* **18**(2):105–113, 2004.
13. See <www.creationontheweb.com/content/view/2679> or Hartnett, J.G., Quasar riddle for big bang astronomy, *J. of Creation* **19**(2):5,6, 2005.
14. See for example, Arp, A., Burbidge, E.M., Chu, Y., Flesch, E., Patat, F., Rupprecht, G., NGC 3628: Ejection activity associated with quasars, *A&A*, **391**:833–840, 2002.

Appendix 6: Light-travel-time problem solved

1. Introduction

Here let us initially confine the following analysis to an expanding universe without matter. The line element is that of cosmological special relativity (CSR) and is given by

$$ds^2 = c^2 dt^2 - (dx^1)^2 - (dx^2)^2 - (dx^3)^2 + \tau^2 dv^2 \quad (A6.1)$$

where τ is the Hubble–Carmeli time constant. The coordinate v is the Hubble expansion velocity of the cosmos, the radial speed of the expanding fabric of space; x^1, x^2 and x^3 are spatial coordinates; and t is atomic time as recorded by Earth-based clocks. The null condition $ds = 0$ describes the Hubble expansion with no gravity, but this also requires $dt = 0$.

γ factor in special relativity

Writing $dr^2 = (dx^1)^2 + (dx^2)^2 + (dx^3)^2$ in arbitrary spatial coordinates, (A6.1) becomes

$$ds^2 = c^2 dt^2 \left(1 - \frac{dr^2}{c^2 dt^2} + \frac{\tau^2}{c^2} \frac{dv^2}{dt^2} \right). \quad (A6.2)$$

Now dividing by ds^2,

$$1 = c^2 \left(\frac{dt}{ds} \right)^2 \left(1 - \frac{u^2}{c^2} + \frac{\tau^2}{c^2} \left(\frac{dv}{dt} \right)^2 \right), \quad \text{(A6.3)}$$

where $u = dr/dt$. Therefore the relativistic γ factor is

$$\gamma_E = c \frac{dt}{ds} = \left(1 - \frac{u^2}{c^2} + \frac{\tau^2}{c^2} \left(\frac{dv}{dt} \right)^2 \right)^{-1/2}. \quad \text{(A6.4)}$$

And when $dv/dt \to 0$,

$$\gamma_E = \left(1 - \frac{u^2}{c^2} \right)^{-1/2}, \quad \text{(A6.5)}$$

as per Einstein's special relativity (SR). This is because SR does not deal with an expanding space; that is, v is identically zero. The result is the usual γ factor in SR, which causes strange relativistic effects (time dilation and length contraction) at high relative speeds; that is, where $u \to c$. Besides, on the local scale, the universe is not expanding now.

γ factor in cosmological special relativity

Similarly, from (A6.1) it follows that

$$ds^2 = \tau^2 dv^2 \left(1 - \frac{dr^2}{\tau^2 dv^2} + \frac{c^2}{\tau^2} \frac{dt^2}{dv^2} \right). \quad \text{(A6.6)}$$

Dividing by ds^2,

$$1 = \tau^2 \left(\frac{dv}{ds}\right)^2 \left(1 - \frac{t_c^2}{\tau^2} + \frac{c^2}{\tau^2}\left(\frac{dt}{dv}\right)^2\right), \quad \text{(A6.7)}$$

where $t_c = dr/dv$ is cosmic time measured backwards from $t_c = 0$ at the observer, but determined from the expansion. By contrast, t is the locally measured atomic time. Therefore the relativistic γ factor is

$$\gamma_C = \tau\frac{dv}{ds} = \left(1 - \frac{t_c^2}{\tau^2} + \frac{c^2}{\tau^2}\left(\frac{dt}{dv}\right)^2\right)^{-1/2}. \quad \text{(A6.8)}$$

When dv/dt is large compared to $a_0 = c/\tau$,

$$\gamma_C = \left(1 - \frac{t_c^2}{\tau^2}\right)^{-1/2}, \quad \text{(A6.9)}$$

as per Carmeli's CSR.[1] This is the normal case in the cosmos in CSR. The motion of the galaxies is dominated by the expansion, and local motions are negligibly small. Since $t_c = dr/dv \rightarrow \tau$, this γ factor causes velocity dilation and length contraction analogous to that in SR.

2. Lorentz transformations

Since we assume Hubble Law to be axiomatically true, $v \approx H_0 r$; therefore locally,

$$\frac{dv}{dt} \approx H_0 \frac{dr}{dt}. \quad \text{(A6.10)}$$

Hence, it follows that $dv/dt \to 0$ as $dr/dt \to 0$. We know that local space is not expanding. Therefore it follows from (A6.2) that we can set $dv/dt \to 0$ in (A6.4), resulting in (A6.5), and hence space and time coordinates transform according to the usual Lorentz transformations in SR:

$$r' = \gamma_E (r - ut) \qquad \text{(A6.11a)}$$

$$t' = \gamma_E (t - ur/c^2). \qquad \text{(A6.11b)}$$

In cosmology, space and velocity coordinates transform by the cosmological transformation[1]

$$r' = \gamma_C (r - t_c v) \qquad \text{(A6.12a)}$$

$$v' = \gamma_C (v - t_c r / \tau^2). \qquad \text{(A6.12b)}$$

Comparing the above transformations shows that the cosmological transformation can be formally obtained from the Lorentz transformation by changing t to v and c to τ. Thus, the transfer from ordinary physics to the expanding universe, under the above assumption of empty space, for null four-vectors is simply achieved by replacing u/c by t_c/τ, where t_c is the cosmic time measured with respect to us now.

3. Time dilation

Let us now suppose that the observer is located at the centre of the expansion. Let us also represent the time interval recorded by an inertial clock, co-moving with expanding sources[2] attached to space as dT and the local Earth-based atomic time interval as dt. From (A6.2), we can write

$$\frac{dT}{dt} = \frac{ds}{cdt} = \gamma_E^{-1}. \qquad \text{(A6.13)}$$

Let us assume that motion through space is negligible. Therefore, with $u \to 0$,

$$dt = dT\left(1 + \frac{\tau^2}{c^2}\left(\frac{dv}{dt}\right)^2\right)^{-1/2}. \qquad \text{(A6.14)}$$

At the present epoch, $dv/dt = 0$, because we observe no expansion. This means, except for curvature effects, which are presently ignored, clocks in the universe run at essentially the same rate as on Earth. However, if dv/dt was much greater than $a_0 = c/\tau$ (a universal constant), it follows that $dt << dT$. I propose that this was the case during Day 4 of Creation Week, and vast amounts of time passed on the galaxies expanding out from the centre of the universe, with little time passing at the centre.

What we now observe in the universe is the redshifted light from the galaxies, which has resulted from the expansion, not from this time-dilation mechanism. The light is continuing to travel towards the earth from the distant galaxies, as it has for billions of years by cosmological clocks, but because Earth clocks now run at the same rate, we only observe expansion effects. The reference clocks in the cosmos are these cosmological, or Hubble, clocks, which can be related to redshift z by

$$\frac{t_c}{\tau} = \frac{(1+z)^2 - 1}{(1+z)^2 + 1}. \qquad (A6.15)$$

As $z \to \infty$, we are seeing back towards the beginning of time, where $t_c \to \tau \approx 13.54$ billion years. But because this observation does not take into account the episode of rapid expansion (which is not observable today), the universal constant τ more correctly describes the size of the universe, not its true age as measured by Earth clocks.

One-way speed of light

We can write (A6.1) as

$$ds^2 = c^2 dt^2 - dr^2 + \tau^2 dv^2, \qquad (A6.16)$$

where $dr^2 = (dx^1)^2 + (dx^2)^2 + (dx^3)^2$. Dividing (A6.16) by dt^2, and equating $ds = 0$ for the trajectory of a photon in *spacetimevelocity*, we get

$$\left(\frac{dr}{dt}\right)^2 = c^2 \left(1 + \frac{1}{a_0^2}\left(\frac{dv}{dt}\right)^2\right). \qquad (A6.17)$$

The speed of light, c, in (A6.17) is actually the locally measured two-way speed. The speed dr/dt is not the measurable two-way speed of light, c, but the non-measurable one-way speed of light.[3,4] It tells us the speed of the expansion with respect to local Earth-based atomic clocks. Notice if dv/dt is zero we get the usual limiting speed c of SR. However, if dv/dt was extremely large in the unobservable past in the vicinity of Earth, as it now appears to be in the cosmos, which is in our past, then the one-way speed of light was also much larger then.

The apparent effect on the one-way speed of light, dr/dt, is really the direct result of *time dilation*. The actual measurable speed of light has not changed. It is *time* that is the variable in these equations, and as a result *only appears* to be producing enormous theoretical changes in the one-way speed of light, as seen by the observer. The actual speed of light is always the two-way speed c and is constant.

Spherically symmetric universe

From (A6.16), it may be noted that this result is true in general for any coordinate system. In the real universe, I consider the case of spherically symmetric coordinates, but it should be remembered that the time dilation is not the result of the choice of a coordinate frame.

In a spherically symmetric, isotropic expanding[5] universe, evenly filled with matter of density Ω, it can be shown that for a photon trajectory:

$$\left(\frac{dr}{dt}\right)^2 = c^2 \left[1 + (1-\Omega)\left(\frac{r}{c\tau}\right)^2\right]\left[1 + \frac{1}{a_0^2}\left(\frac{dv}{dt}\right)^2\right], \quad \text{(A6.18)}$$

where the effects of adding matter have been included in (A6.17). Here, Ω is the averaged matter density of the universe expressed as a fraction of the critical density. The additional term results from solving the

Carmelian 4D *spacevelocity* representation of the large-scale structure of the universe.

At the current epoch, anywhere in the universe (A6.17) holds. That means that the local physics is determined solely by SR, as expected, because dv/dt measured against local clocks is zero. However, at past epochs, dv/dt is non-zero and CSR must be applied instead. When matter is added, on a sufficiently large scale, the situation changes and we use (A6.18). This means (A6.18) is only really valid in a neighbourhood of a universe that is spherically symmetric around the origin—hence it must involve an isotropic matter distribution. Homogeneity is not required.

4. Light-travel time

In order to calculate the light-travel time in the universe from light sources at the edge, we need to know the speed of the photons in terms of atomic time as measured by Earth clocks, which underwent a period of massive time dilation during the first days of creation, especially on Day 4, when the Creator created the heavenly bodies. This is not the speed of light in terms of cosmic time, which is always c, and since Earth clocks now tick at the same rate as cosmic clocks, c is the locally measured value now also. So we need to know dr/dt, where r is the proper distance to the source and t is atomic time units on Earth.

We have observed in (A6.8) that the value of dv/dt needs to be very large at high redshifts ($z \gg 0$) at

Figure A6.1. Acceleration defined by (A6.20) is plotted against redshift or time. Redshift is indicated and increasing towards the right and time from the creation as increasing towards the left. The scale of the axes are arbitrary, except for the origin. The solid curve indicates that at some time during creation the acceleration was switched from an extremely large number to zero. The broken exponential curve indicates that this may have occurred very rapidly but not instantaneously. In order to model this in (A6.20)–(A6.23) the exponential curve was chosen.

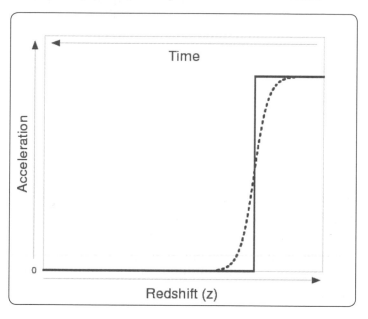

cosmic times $t_c \gg 0$, but from (A6.4) it is clear dv/dt needs to be zero at the current epoch $t_c = 0$ ($z \approx 0$). This is best described by a step function

$$
\left.
\begin{aligned}
\frac{1}{a_0}\frac{dv}{dt} &\to \infty \;:\; z \gg 0 \\[2mm]
\frac{1}{a_0}\frac{dv}{dt} &= 0 \;:\; z \approx 0
\end{aligned}
\right\}
\qquad (A6.19)
$$

as shown in the solid curve in fig. A6.1. The function (A6.19) is shown with a finite maximum value, which, at this stage, we can only say was extremely large. This means that at the Creation the acceleration dv/dt was very large and then at some value of redshift $z \approx 0$ the acceleration was switched to, or rapidly decreased to, zero. This switching was physically associated with the stretching of the fabric of space itself, as God spread out the heavens.

Now the function (A6.19) can be approximated by an exponential of the form

$$\frac{1}{a_0}\frac{dv}{dt} = \left[\exp\left(\frac{\eta t_c}{\tau}\right) - 1 \right]^{1/2}, \qquad \text{(A6.20)}$$

where η is a dimensionless proportionality constant that is yet to be determined. The function in (A6.20) has the needed characteristics and can be related to redshift z, using (A6.15). This function is also illustrated by the broken curve in fig. A6.1, where a maximum value has been imposed. However, for the purpose of the following calculations, (A6.20) is used instead, which increases without bound as $t_c \to \tau$ or as $z \to \infty$.

From a comparison of the magnitudes of the terms in (A6.18), the matter density term can be neglected for the purposes of calculating the light-travel time in the universe in terms of Earth atomic time units. It follows from (A6.18), with $\Omega = 1$ and (A6.20), that

$$\frac{dr}{dt} = c \exp\left(\frac{\eta t_c}{2\tau}\right) \qquad \text{(A6.21)}$$

Figure A6.2. The light-travel time (in Earth days) is plotted against distance in the universe (in units of $c\tau$) for two choices of the dimensionless free parameter $\eta = 10^{12}$ (solid curve) and 10^{13} (broken curve). Both curves become flat, meaning that the light travels the rest of the distance to the limits of the universe in the time shown.

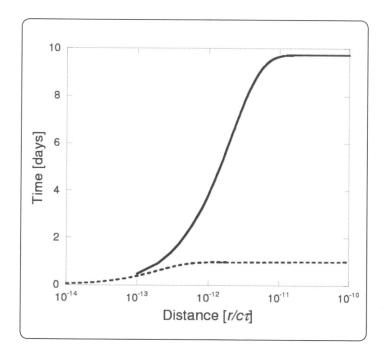

is the one-way speed of light; the speed light travels toward the observer at the origin of a spherically symmetric universe, determined from the proper distances which the photons travel but with respect to local Earth-based atomic clocks. Note that (A6.17) does not depend on spherical matter symmetry; it only applies to an empty universe.

Into (A6.21) we can substitute $t_c/\tau \rightarrow v/c$, where v is the expansion speed. Now I make the assumption that the Hubble Law ($v \approx r/\tau$) also applied at the creation. Therefore it follows that

$$\frac{1}{c}\frac{dr}{dt} \approx \exp\left(\frac{\eta}{2}\frac{r}{c\tau}\right). \qquad (A6.22)$$

By integrating (A6.22), we can calculate the distance light travelled in atomic time t:

$$t \approx \frac{2\tau}{\eta}\left[1 - \exp\left(-\frac{\eta}{2}\frac{r}{c\tau}\right)\right]. \qquad (A6.23)$$

With $c = 1$ light-year/year and the chosen value of $\tau = 13.54$ billion years, the distance scale $c\tau = 13.54$ billion light-years. The light-travel time has been calculated from (A6.23) using $\eta = 10^{12}$ and 10^{13}, and is shown in fig. A6.2. For large r in (A6.23), the light-travel time t approaches a maximum value of $2\tau/\eta$. The result is an exponentially rising function that means light fills the universe to vast distances within one day (by Earth-based clocks), assuming the value of $\eta = 10^{13}$. Depending on the exact magnitude of the undetermined parameter, the light-travel time was only about a day as measured by Earth-based clocks. (See broken curve in fig. A6.2.)

Estimates for the size and extent of the acceleration term dv/dt may vary. At the present epoch, in our local vicinity, it is identically zero because the environment of the solar system is designed for life. In the past it was enormously larger, as evidenced by the cosmos, as we have seen. This acceleration was switched off during Creation Week. Light from the most distant sources reached Earth within only a day (measured on Earth clocks) before that. Now about six thousand years have passed since that time, so it takes light from those same sources an extra six or so thousand years to get here. Therefore it appears that this theory solves what has long seemed to be an intractable problem.

References

1. See Carmeli, M., Hartnett, J.G. and Oliveira, F.J., The cosmic time in terms of the redshift, *Found. Phys. Lett.* **19**(3):277–283, 2006, <arxiv.org/abs/gr-qc/0506079>; Carmeli, M., *Cosmological Special Relativity*, 2nd ed. World Scientific, Singapore, 2002, p. 15, section 2.11.
2. These sources are subject to the Hubble Law $\tau\,dv=dr$.
3. Hartnett, J.G., Distant starlight and Genesis: is 'observed time' a physical reality? *J. of Creation* **16**(1):65–67, 2002.
4. Newton, R., Distant starlight and Genesis: conventions of time measurement, *J. of Creation* **15**(1):80–85, 2001.
5. Hartnett, J.G., Cosmological expansion in a creationist cosmology, *J. of Creation* **19**(3):96–102, 2005.

Recommended Reading

Dismantling the Big Bang by Alex Williams and John Hartnett reveals the scientific and philosophical weaknesses at the core of big-bang thinking and the contradictions to which they lead. Written on a level that lay-people can understand, it shows the intellectual superiority of the history of the universe given in the Bible as a basis for our thinking about the cosmos. Rediscover how to think about the universe in the only way that makes sense—from God's perspective, in the light of the history given in His Word.

The Creation Answers Book provides biblical answers to over 60 important questions that everyone wants to know on creation/evolution and the Bible! Not only does it answer your own questions, but equips you to effectively respond to those that resist the gospel due to worldly teaching on origins. This important work is a 'must-have' for anyone's library!

AUSTRALIA
Creation Ministries International (Australia)
PO Box 4545,
Eight Mile Plains,
Qld 4113
Phone: (07) 3340 9888
Fax: (07) 3340 9889

CANADA
Creation Ministries International (Canada)
5-420 Erb St West,
Suite 213,
Waterloo, Ontario,
N2L 6K6
Phone: (519) 746 7616
Fax: (519) 746 7617

NEW ZEALAND
Creation Ministries International (New Zealand)
PO Box 39005,
Howick, Auckland 2145
Phone/Fax: (09) 537 4818

SINGAPORE
Creation Ministries International (Singapore)
Refer to <www.creationontheweb.com/contactus> for details

SOUTH AFRICA
Creation Ministries International (South Africa)
PO Box 3349,
Durbanville 7551
Phone: (021) 979 0107
Fax: (086) 519 0555

UK/EUROPE
Creation Ministries International (UK/Europe)
15 Station St,
Whetstone, Leicestershire,
LE8 6JS
Phone: 0845-6800-264 (CMI)

USA
Creation Ministries International (USA)
4355 J Cobb Pkwy,
PMB 218,
Atlanta GA 30339-3887
Phone: 1-800-6161-CMI
Fax: (404) 420 2247

OTHER COUNTRIES
Creation Ministries International
PO Box 4545,
Eight Mile Plains,
Qld 4113 Australia
Phone: (+61 7) 3340 9888
Fax: (+61 7) 3340 9889